COTTON TEETH

GLENN ROCKOWITZ

OTHER BOOKS BY GLENN ROCKOWITZ
Rodeo In Joliet

The following is a true story. One in which names have been changed, time has been
compressed, and certain people have been composited into single characters. The only
exception to that rule is the individual identified in the book as "Bob," whose real name is,
in fact, Bob. Why? Because Bob is a dick.

HARPER CASE

Harper & Case
511 Avenue of the Americas
New York, NY 10011
contact: info@harpercase.com

Library of Congress Control Number: 2009941535
ISBN: 978-0-578-24956-8 (paperback)
            978-0-578-25708-2 (hardcover)
            978-0-578-25709-9 (ebook)

Printed in the United States by the first book manufacturer to join the Green Press Initiative,
using sustainable and environmentally responsible practices. FSC & Rainforest Alliance
certified. 100 % recycled, 30 % post-consumer waste, acid-free paper.

"May the jaws of death have cotton teeth."
—Tom Robbins, *Jitterbug Perfume*

PROLOGUE
a small writing desk in seattle, 2019

I get it. I usually skip the prologue too. This one might actually
be worth the five minutes, though. I'll even try to spice it up a little
in case it winds up being the only part you read. Which, again,
I totally get. You're a busy person.

The bottom line is this:

This book took me almost ten years to write.

That's right. Ten fucking years.

Hey. Don't get all judgey.

I actually wrote and re-wrote the entire book several times during
those ten years.

I know. I'm an idiot.

But at least I am, and was, an idiot for a good reason.

A reason I didn't fully understand until recently, until well after I
had already written and re-written hundreds of thousands of words
over the course of thousands of hours. A reason that ultimately saved
me from releasing a book I knew deep down would never feel truly
complete or right.

So, no. This book didn't take so long to write because I spent years
toiling over finding *just the right words* or trying to perfect some kind
of magical rhythmic structure.

If you read my first book, you already know how few shits I give in
this regard.

And if you *haven't* read my first book, well, please email me and let
me know how it feels to live a life without joy, passion or mirth.

I really want to know.

Relax. I'm kidding, Mom.

The reason this book never felt ready is simple:

I was too afraid to write about certain events in my life that I believe
played a significant role in making me who I am today and even more
afraid to lean into the pain I knew the memories of those events would
invariably bring.

But isn't that why a person writes a memoir in the first place, Greg?!

Yes it is. (And it's Glenn.)

The book you hold in your hand right now is the book I believe I was
supposed to write all along.

It just wasn't time until now, apparently.

How do I know?

Well, some crazy shit happened recently.

Shit that felt way too specific to be purely coincidental.

Let me set the scene while you feed the cats and top off
your chardonnay:

March, 2017.

A desolate cemetery.

A hot, cloudless afternoon.

Sweat dripping from my brow as I shoveled dirt onto a coffin,
trying to decide how best to eulogize the man inside it:
Ronnie, my stepfather, a man I had known for so long and loved
so deeply.

I hadn't prepared a speech because I knew I only wanted
to share two very brief stories:

The first about the afternoon Ron and I went to the grocery store
together to buy a birthday cake for my mother and the woman behind
the bakery counter asked us what we wanted the cake to say, to which
Ron replied, "Oh, sorry. We don't want a talking cake."

The other about the day Ronnie taught me how to drive stick shift—
or 'manual transmission' for you Mensa types—and how we sat stalled
and frozen in the middle of a busy intersection while drivers around us
honked their horns and cursed at us through their windows, all while
he calmly instructed me to ignore the assholes and remember that
everything worth having lives on the other side of fear.

I thought a lot about those words in the days following the funeral.

The days in which, coincidentally, the aforementioned *crazy shit*
started happening.

It went like this:

A week after Ronnie's funeral, I received an email from a total stranger
offering condolences.

Which led to:

The discovery of a shared experience this stranger and I had over
30 years earlier.

Which led to:

This stranger reconnecting me with several other people from my
childhood with the same shared experience, one of whom had actually
attended Ronnie's funeral.

Which led to:
Breakfasts, lunches, phone calls and Skype conversations with all those people to discuss the details of our long-ago shared experience during the summer of 1977.
Which led to:
The validation of memories none of us had ever talked about with anyone outside our therapists, and maybe a single trusted person in each of our lives.
Which led to:
The sad reminder that I had just buried my single trusted person.
Throughout those weeks of reconnecting and reminiscing, I kept hearing Ronnie's words.
Everything worth having lives on the other side of fear.
And it was those words that made me realize why all the previous versions of this book were never quite right.
I was too scared to push my way through the fear.
I was too scared to write about things that played an essential part in the full and honest story of my life.
I knew that if this book was ever going to be what I wanted it to be, I would have to ignore those blaring car horns and cursing drivers in my head, step on the gas, and drive right into the fucking void.
And now here we are.
I hope to see you on the other side.

bathroom floor

Everything is black, my heart is a hummingbird, my lungs are in my throat and I don't know if I'm flying or if I'm falling. The doctors say I won't know which until I hit the ground.

But this is it: a volcanic surge of fear and nausea and fucking dread I feel every day now. Sometimes once, sometimes every few minutes. Either way, I don't know how much longer I can keep living on my heels like this. Always off-balance, brittle fists up and ready.

Nine minutes ago, I was lying in bed next to my father and we were both fast asleep and quietly dreaming. Now I'm curled up and trembling on his bathroom floor, stress-packed between the toilet and the sink like a cat on moving day. I'm trying to catch my breath, trying to shake loose the shock of seeing the calendar tacked to the wall beside his bed. The shock of seeing that date.

outside an emergency room

Today is the day I'm supposed to be dead but I'm not.
Instead, I'm watching my father circle a hospital parking lot in a minivan
the graywhite color of bird shit.
Lap after lap through dead, oily snow, the sad hissing of rubber against
frozen asphalt, swelling and fading over and over with each full lap.
I count the dying seconds as he circles the lot.
Seventy-six.
I count to calm myself.
Ninety-eight.
I've counted to calm myself ever since I was little.
A hundred sixty seconds.
Hissing crackling swelling fading—the sound of one full lap.
A hundred ninety.
Hissing crackling swelling fading—another one.
Two-hundred eighty-four.
Hissing crackling swelling fading.
Speed it up, old man.
I lean against the concrete post in front of the emergency room doors and
I tilt my face toward the sky and I close my eyes and let the small break
of sunlight soak my face.
The rays coming through the small rip in the snow clouds are a tiny
window of blue sky that I know will close just as swiftly as it opened.
I know this because the sun has been lying to me my whole life and
it's a lie I've gotten used to.

Four-hundred twenty-seven.

The soundtrack of the hospital plays out behind me:

A distant yell. *Fuuuuck.*

A stranger's voice, resolute and confident, *move move move.*

A metallic clank-pop of a gurney.

A pained guttural moan, a scream held in by a hand, *gunshot wound upper right quadrant.*

I smell blood, taste it in the air, taste it on my tongue like an old penny.

Five-hundred twenty-three.

Hissing crackling swelling fading.

How many laps is he going to do in this fucking parking lot?

Hissing crackling swelling fading.

Suddenly, there's a deep, muffled voice behind me, a car door opening, the same deep voice now sharp.

"Just walk the fuck in there and tell 'em what's wrong. I'll be right behind you, Sweetie."

A child's trembling voice replies, a voice too young for a gender, a voice too young to be dropped off in front of a hospital alone.

"But where do I—?"

The rest of the small trembling voice gets drowned out by a muffler as a car drives away.

Then, a cry.

A breathless cry, a lost scared cry.

I open my eyes and I shield the sun with my hand and I turn around and connect the cry to the mouth.

A young girl—*six? seven?*—too young to be left alone.

Chapped alabaster face, small purpling lips, straw-colored hair tented and tangled with sleep.

I walk over and I crouch down and I soften my voice.

"You're okay, you're okay, what're you looking for?"

She has no words, just crying breaths.

"You see that big white desk right inside the doors?"

She nods through a stuttered inhale.

"Just go over there and tell the lady what's hurting you, okay? I'll wait right here. All *you* have to do is wave to me when you're safe. Easy enough, right?"

She can't catch her breath.

Too young to be left alone.

I want to pick her up and carry her inside and tell the nurse behind the counter that she's my daughter, that my daughter is hurting, that I need them to help her, *please help my daughter.*

I want to do all of this, but I know that I can't.

I'm a twenty-eight-year-old adult male and the numbers say I'm unsafe and the numbers are right.

While I'm not one of those numbers, she needs to trust those numbers, she needs to trust the science of violence.

"It's okay. I'll be right here. All you have to do is walk in there and talk to the lady behind the counter."

She exhales and cracks a half smile.

"But then you *have* to wave to me, so I know you're okay. And if you're *really* lucky I'll wave back."

The half smile becomes a full smile.

She turns and steps onto the magic rubber carpet that opens the sliding glass doors, walks to the front desk, sees me giving her the thumbs-up and smiles. A short olive-skinned woman in scrubs walks out from behind the desk, smiles at her, grabs her hand and leads her away.

No wave?

She didn't wave.

What an asshole.

I laugh at my own thought and I walk back to the concrete post and I shade my eyes and see that my father is still circling the same fifty parking spots.

Hissing crackling swelling fading.

Stopping.

Finally.

Silence.

Six-hundred twenty-three seconds.

The sun dips behind the thickening clouds and the snow kicks up.

Six-hundred twenty-three seconds to find a fucking parking spot.

Six-hundred twenty-three seconds we don't have.

I see him in the distance as he kicks open the car door, braces his upper body between the inside handle and the doorframe and rocks back and forth until he's up onto his feet.

My chest turns to concrete.

Fifty-seven years old and navigating his way across the parking lot like he's ninety, teetering across the icy crosswalk like a newborn giraffe staggering across piano keys.

As I wait, I close my eyes again and think about that night—that God-sized night exactly three months ago today.

That broken, black night in my doctor's office when I sat frozen and hypnotized by the glow of the X-rays pinned against the light box, desperately trying to hold onto the floor to keep myself from falling into the sky forever.

Of the hundreds of words that spilled from my doctor's mouth that night, I heard only six:

"Cancer. Everywhere. Three months at best."

I was twenty-eight-years old, my wife was eight-and-a-half months pregnant, and I had just been told cancer was *everywhere* and I had three months left on earth.

Three months at best.

Three fucking months.

I had no symptoms. No pains, no lumps, no rashes, no bumps, no marks, no scratches, no sores, no fucking anything.

I'd just been tired, bone tired, for years.

Years of different doctors telling me not to worry, telling me I was too young to be sick, telling me I worked too much, telling me it was nothing, telling me it was all in my head, telling me I had nothing to worry about.

Years of *nothing to worry about.*

And now the *nothing to worry about* was scattered all over my body and there wasn't a goddamn thing I could do about it.

I was twenty-eight-years old, my wife was eight-and-a-half months pregnant and I had three months left to live.

Today is that day, exactly three months later.

Today is the day I'm supposed to be dead and I'm not.

hospital entrance, forty-three seconds later

My father's voice snaps me from my daze.
"Whatcha smiling about?"
"It took you almost fifteen minutes to find a spot."
"I'm in a lot of pain if you hadn't noticed, Stuie."
My middle name is Stuart and he's called me Stuie since I was little and
there's a love shape to it that calms me.
"I could've dropped you off at the front entrance, parked the car myself
and met you inside, Dad."
"Why didn't you suggest that earlier?!"
I did.
I'd offered to drop him off in front of the hospital several times on our
way here, and he knows this. The smile in his voice tells me so.
I slip my arm into his and we make our way onto the magic rubber
carpet and through the sliding glass doors and down the maze of hospital
hallways that lead to the elevator.
Odors fill the spaces where our words should be.
Shit and piss and antiseptic and vomit.
No words. Just smells.
I spot the-little-girl-who-didn't-love-me-enough-to-wave sitting in a chair
alone at the end of the hallway, legs sticking straight out, her tiny body
L-shaped and scared.
"Hold on, Pop."
"C'mon, Stu. I don't wanna be late."
"Just wait here, Dad. I'll be back in a sec."

He lets out one of his signature dramatic sighs. The kind of sigh someone would let out if you'd just asked them to help you move a piano in Phoenix during the summer without pay.

"Oh, keep your diaper on, Pop."

I make my way toward the girl with the trembling voice, the Alone Girl Too Young To Be Left Alone and I crouch down next to her and watch her eyes loosen when she recognizes my face.

"Are they taking good care of you?"

She says *yes* too quickly, as if it was already chambered behind a dozen others.

I point to my father leaning against the wall next to the elevator and I ask her if she sees the old man who looks like a sad turtle and the corners of her mouth curl upwards as she nods another *yes*, this one lighter.

"That turtle's my dad. His name's *Melvin*."

She smiles.

"Pretty dumb name, right?"

She nods and she smiles and she starts to air-swim with her legs.

I ask her where *her* dad is and she shrugs.

A gaunt female nurse with wiry gray hair interrupts and asks me if I'm Lila's father.

Lila.

I tell her I'm not, tell her I just wanted to make sure Lila is being taken care of, tell her I found Lila alone in front of the hospital earlier.

The nurse seems uneasy with both my explanation and my presence and I don't fault her for it.

I extend my hand and I smile and I tell her my name is Glenn and I tell her I'm here with my dad. I tell her I just want to make sure Lila finds her own dad.

"Melvin!"

Lila's voice is steady, buttery as it cuts in.

"*Melvin*. You remembered!"

I tell the nurse I'll be upstairs if she needs me for anything.

She forces a smile, gives me a reluctant thank-you, cups her hand around Lila's shoulder and tells Lila to follow her to the X-ray room.

X-ray? Did someone hurt her?

"Stuie."

My father calls out to me as I watch Lila and the nurse make their way down the hallway. They get smaller and smaller with each step.

Things usually feel better the smaller they get, but there's no comfort in this kind of small.

I turn and I walk back to the elevator and I tell my father *I can't wait all day*. I hold the doors open for him, tell him to *move his ass*, tell him I don't want to be late for the appointment.

I've been a comedian for years and this kind of ball-busting is my way of softening pain and breaking tension. A coping mechanism I picked up long ago.

He doesn't laugh and I don't blame him.

He's right. Now is not the time for my bullshit.

"What the hell were you doing down there, Glenn?"

"Some guy dropped that little girl off in front of the ER during the two months you were looking for a parking spot."

"I doubt he just 'left her there alone' and took off. She's too young for that."

Exactly.

Seven years old is too young to be left alone.

silver horseshoe summer camp, 1977, day 1

The pine trees right outside our cabin window are leaning back like
they're going to tip over. Like they're trying to get away from something
I can't see. It could be a monster or it could be an alien or it could be a
dinosaur but it looks like they've been trying to run away for a long time
because they don't reach toward the sky like normal trees.
People probably think slanty trees like these ones are broken.
They probably think the good ones are the trees that get to grow far away
from the ocean. The ones that never have to fight all that wind. The ones
with their legs buried deep underground.
But I think trees like these slanty ones are stronger because they've
probably been fighting the wind from the day they popped out of the dirt.
I could sit here on my bunk and stare at them forever.
I'd rather just go home.
The other kids in my cabin won't stop running around and screaming
because they're excited for the fun and the sun and the campfires and the
games and the songs and all the stuff in the brochure my dad showed me:
the *crystal-clear streams*
the *rolling wildflower fields*
the *bright white sun*
Mom says that even though I'll be here for twenty-four sleeps, I'll hardly
notice because I'll be having so much *fun*.
She always says *fun* in a way that makes me never want to have it.
Dad says whatever I do, do *not* have fun.
I know he thinks it's funny because he laughs every time he says it.
"Whatever you do, Stuie, do *not* have fun!"

It's not funny.

I've done seven years of sleeps at home until today and I've been happy with that.

Even when my mom and dad are yelling at each other in the next room, I'm happy because I'm used to it.

The red-haired boy on the bunk below me keeps kicking my mattress, and I laugh because I don't want to cry even though crying is all I want to do right now.

I pick up my pillow and move it to the other side of the bunk and I get into a nap position even though I'm just trying to get my ears closer to the cabin door so I can hear the conversation my mom is having on the front porch with the guy I think is going to be in charge of us for the next twenty-four sleeps.

He is tall and wide and strong like a lion and that makes me feel a little safer.

I watch them through the crack between my pillow and the metal bar at the end of the bunk. His hands are on his hips and he leans toward her to catch all the words she's speaking so quietly. His mop of dirty blonde curls bounces with each *yeah got it*.

He looks like he's in charge of the world.

I hear my mom tell him I wet my bed every night and I see the corners of his eyes get soft the way they do when grown-ups try not to laugh. I know this face because I see this face a lot.

And even though it embarrasses me and makes me feel broken, I try not to think about it too much. If I think about it too much I will cry and I cry too much.

That's what other kids say. *You cry too much, Glenn.*

I wish my mom would tell him that I have *special needs* so I don't have to feel bad for everything I do and for everything I feel.

She reaches into her purse and hands the lion a small orange bottle filled with little red pills. These are the medicine candies I got from the doctor before I left and I am supposed to swallow one every night before bed so I don't wet the bed.

The lion holds it up to the sun and shakes it like he doesn't believe pills can stop a kid from wetting the bed.

I don't believe pills can stop a kid from wetting the bed either but I want to believe it more than I've ever wanted to believe anything.

My mom keeps talking to the lion about stupid things because she's run out of important things.

"I almost wish I was the one going to summer camp. It all looks like so much fun."

The lion smiles and puts his hand on the side of her arm.

"So much fun. We have so many things planned, Glenn won't have time to miss you guys."

"I bet! It's funny because when *I* was a kid…"

Her voice fades into a flat kind of grown-up talk.

Every time I hear grown-ups talk like this, I imagine Styrofoam pellets spilling out of their mouths and filling up the whole room, because that's what it sounds like to me.

Like they're trying to ship something in a box that's way too big for what's inside.

Spilling *SuchBeautifulWeather*

Spilling *We'reOrginallyFromNewYork*

Spilling *WeLiveInPhoenixNow*

Spilling *wordswordswords* spillingspillingspilling

As the front porch floods with Styrofoam, the lion turns to me and smiles at me in a way I don't really understand. It doesn't look silly and it doesn't look happy and it doesn't look calm or warm or safe. It's a smile that doesn't look like a smile. It looks like a fist.

"Hey fag!"

A kid's voice followed by a kick.

My mattress bows in the middle like a volcano and I lean my head over the side of the bunk and I speak to the floor.

"What?"

The boy lying on the bed below me laughs.

"You just admitted you're a fag!"

"No I didn't."

My eyes start to burn and I know the tears are coming. I don't want to cry but I can tell he already knows I'm weak.

"What's your name, fag?"

Don't tell him.

"Glenn."

He laughs again and hops off his bunk and stands in front of me and I can smell mustard on his hand as he sticks it out.

"Corey."

I shake his hand and he holds onto mine and he pulls me closer to him until most of my body is hanging off the edge like the awning over our back door at home.

11

"Why are you a fag, Glenn?"
My heart is pounding and my voice feels soft and weird.
"I'm not sure."
His face changes shape.
"Do you even know what a fag is?"
"Of course I do!"
"What is it then, fag?"
Silence.
I can feel my face turn red.
"Someone who pees the bed."
He crinkles his forehead.
"What?"
"A fag is someone who pees the bed."
Silence.
Corey tilts his head the way my friend's dog does when someone plays
the harmonica.
"So we're *both* fags?"
My heart slows.
"What?"
"I'm a fag too, Glenn."
"You pee the bed?"
He shrugs yes and I'm confused but now I'm comfortable.
"How did you know I was a fag?"
"I heard your mom tell Randy."
"Who's Randy?"
Corey points to the lion, now spilling Styrofoam at my dad's feet.
"*That* guy. He's our counselor."
"I figured, but no one introduced me to him."
"Shit. *I'll* do it. C'mon."
I climb off the bunk like a three-legged cat and hit the floor with
a thud and we walk out to the porch and I say nothing because I
know it's rude to interrupt grown-ups even when they're spilling.
Corey doesn't care.
"Hey Randy. This is Glenn. You didn't meet him yet."
My mom looks at Corey like he just set himself on fire but Corey doesn't
care and I love that he doesn't care and I stick my hand out and I say
my name.
Randy wraps his giant paw around it and he squeezes way too hard and
he smiles another not-smile.

"Nice to meet you, Glenn. I was just telling your folks about how much fun we're gonna have for the next few weeks."

My dad looks at his watch and clears his throat.

"Well, kiddo. Looks like you're in good hands with Randy here."

I beg both of them with my eyes.

Please don't go.

I don't want them to leave me here.

I don't want to be left alone.

Please don't go.

Seven years old is too young to be left alone.

hospital, second floor reception area

The elevator doors open to a sea of empty blue vinyl chairs, a waiting room usually packed with dozens of cancer patients stewing in air thick with sadness and confusion. Apparently, today it's just me and my dad. We wedge ourselves side by side into the two chairs closest to the exit like a captain and navigator on the deck of a sinking ferry. I watch the snow swirl around outside the row of windows at the far side of the room. Hypnotic plumes of powdered sugar.

"Today is three months, Pop."

He turns and looks at me, his eyes suddenly dilated.

"*Today* today?"

"Yup."

He stares at his feet and he speaks through a forced smile.

"Well, ya look good. I think death agrees with you, kiddo."

The last three months had turned my skin to rice paper and my eyes to inverted abalone shells, a sad, wet silver that's finally back to my natural brown.

I force a laugh and I thank him for the sweet sentiment.

All of this is my fault.

The reason why we're even sitting here right now.

The hospitals, the doctors, the pills, the poisons, the needles, the scans, the pain, the pain. The fucking cancer. *His* cancer.

I can still see the green of his eyes spread black the second I told him the News, *my* cancer News, my *three-months-at-best* News.

The secret I hadn't yet told my own wife. I can still hear the styrofoam squeaks of our footsteps in the fresh snow as we walked through his neighborhood in silence.

He prayed for the first time in his life that night.

My atheist father kneeled beside his bed and asked the God he didn't believe in to take away my cancer and give it to him.

Spare my son and take me instead.

He begged that God he didn't believe in.

Spare my son and take me instead.

My atheist father prayed for the first time in his life.

Spare my son and take me instead.

Seven days later, that same God, that God he didn't believe in, said, *careful what you wish for, motherfucker,* and granted him his only wish: *your very own cancer,* end-stage pancreatic, zero chance of survival.

And even though I know the timing was purely and scientifically coincidental—he had been complaining of stomach pains for over a year—the guilt and pain I feel is still a million-acre brushfire in my veins.

"You *do* look good, Stuie. The cancer matches your ey—"

"—Doctor Rockowitz?"

A heavyset nurse in cartoon-patterned scrubs interrupts us as she opens the door two feet from our ship's bridge.

I correct her.

"Oh, he's not a real doctor. He's a psychologist."

"Oh, I'm sorry. *Mister* Rockowitz? Follow me."

My dad shoots me a fuck-you smile.

"Can my Special Needs son come too?"

"Of course!"

I pinch his tush as we make our way down the hallway and he swats my hand away reflexively as though I do it all the time.

I don't.

It's usually something he does to *me.*

He stops and gives me a look that says my pinch is too much, a bridge too far. It's a look I both dread and relish.

"It's such a nice backyard though, Pop."

The nurse props the door open with her foot.

"Have a seat, Mr. Rockowitz. The doctor'll be with you in a minute."

I poke his ribs. "Hear that? A *real* doctor!"

He doesn't smile and he doesn't laugh and I can see his hand shaking on the armrest. I put my arm around him and I pull his head toward me and I kiss his hair. The clock on the wall keeps the rhythm of our silence as we wait.

Forty-six minutes.

I notice the clock on the wall is in a cage for some reason.

Did someone try to steal the clock?

I want to know why that clock is in a cage.

Forty-seven.

We've been sitting in this room for forty-seven fucking minutes.

Forty-eight.

Who tries to steal a fucking clock?

A light knuckle tap on the door as it opens.

The doctor walks in, the wind quietly trying to hold the hem of his white cape. He doesn't say hello and he doesn't apologize for the delay and I remind myself that this is a man we don't have to like. We don't have to have go bowling with him and we don't have to summer with his family on Martha's Vineyard. We just need to let him do his job and have him answer our questions. We need this despite the fact that at all our previous appointments he has barely done the former and has rarely given us space or time for the latter.

He flips open my father's chart and he looks at it like he's seeing it for the very first time.

"Mister Rocko—"

"*Doctor* Rockowitz."

I correct him.

"Everything looks stable."

My dad exhales as I continue.

"Can you be more specific? Just so we have a sense of the bigger picture."

His face reddens slightly and he responds as though I've asked him for a kidney, the periods between his words now visible in the air between us.

"Blood work. Scans. Stable."

Asshole.

"How 'bout in English, not Hollywood Indian."

"Excuse me?"

"More than two words. We're trying to understand exactly what's going on and while *stable* is great, it's not all that helpful. Especially since you've said this is *un-survivable.*"

"Statistically, it is."

"Got it. And we got it weeks ago. We just want to know what *stable* means in terms of time or diet or activity or modifying any of the usual behaviors, ya know?"

His eyes dart back and forth like a ventriloquist dummy waiting for an audience reaction. He speaks.

"Uh. Just keep on doing what you're doing?"

Motherfucker.

"But *what does that mean*?!"

"It means whatever you're doing, just keep doing it."

I can feel the veins in my neck start to flood and throb.

"Doc. We wait *hours* to see you every time we come in and you not only give us under five minutes of your time, but that time is always filled with the kind of vagueness we could get if we were to ask any random person on the street the same questions."

"I'm sorry you feel that way."

"It's not an emotion I need validated. It's pretty straightforward: can you just spend *two minutes* explaining exactly what this cancer *is* so we get a sense of what's going on? I don't think you have any idea what it feels like to live under a giant question mark like this."

His jaw clenches as he speaks.

"Are you done?"

Holy shit.

My dad senses my pending explosion and takes over.

"We understand, Doctor. Thank you."

The doctor says *Thank you, Mister Rockowitz* and bolts out the door. The wind tries to catch his cape in the doorjamb and I appreciate it for trying.

Clunk. Silence.

My heart is a marching snare.

Silence. Silence. Silence.

"He's considered one of the best oncologists in the country, Stuie."

My dad's scared blind faith makes me laugh.

"Who cares if—"

"Glenn. C'mon. Let's be honest. Asking him for a plan or advice at this point is like, I dunno, it's like asking for a brunch menu at Auschwitz."

I lean over and I laugh into his hair and I inhale the sweaty musk of his scalp. The smell calms my heart even though I know my heart has just been dropped onto a raft and cast out to sea.

I want to know why that clock is in a cage.

hospital parking lot, twenty minutes later

We make our way back across the piano-key crosswalk as gusts of frozen
glitter weave through my father's thinning graybrown curls.
It's all so strangely beautiful.
Especially given where we are and why we're here.
I breathe in, hold the frozen air in my chest, breathe out.
All of my breaths feel different now.
A tiny faraway voice bounces off the building walls.
"Melvin!"
I stop and I see Lila waving wildly with both arms like a military mother
seeing her sailors off to war and I wave back just as vigorously.
"What did she just say, Stuie?"
"Nothing. Don't worry about it, Pop."
My father hates his name and he gets upset whenever someone says it out
loud, which is precisely why I told her. I just didn't expect to actually
reap that harvest so soon. Or even at all.
"Melvin!"
Lila and the Man Who Left Her Alone make their way across the snowy
path that bisects the lawn in front of the hospital. When they get past the
crosswalk, Lila jettisons her chaperone and sprints over to us.
I crouch down and I say *how's Lila* and I ask her what the doctors found
out. She struggles to bring me up to speed through labored breaths,
"Nothing's. Wrong. I. Justhave. A..."
She turns around, "Daddy? What do I have?"
He mumbles something at the ground that none of us can make out.

Lila tugs anxiously at the matted fir of her jacket collar.

"Is Melvin all better?"

My father groans under his breath as I speak.

"I don't know, Lila. Why don't you ask *him*?"

She looks up at Annoyed Melvin and she asks if he's *all better*.

He cracks a defeated smile and tells her *almost, Lila*, he's *almost* better.
I know he wants to tell her to stop calling him Melvin but he's too
disarmed by the sadness of her moon-blue eyes.

Lila's father walks by and mumbles *Lila let's go* through his spit-damp
cigarette and flips a strip of greasy brown hair off his face.

My heart ignites when I smell the passing smoke, feel the passing
violence. I stand and I start to follow him.

"Hey!"

Stop, Glenn. What are you doing?

"Hey!"

No. Fuck this guy.

"Stuie!"

There's fear in my father's voice.

"Stuie! Enough. Let's go."

Lila's father stops, turns around. A pile of rock salt crunches under the
weight of his boot. My father sets his hand on the back of Lila's jacket
and speaks calmly, softly.

"Go see your dad, sweetheart."

I crouch down, exhale slowly, ask Lila to give me a high-five, tell her I'm
glad the doctors said she's okay, tell her I'll race her to her car. She bolts
over to her father's legs and she wraps her arms around them. He pries
them off and tells her to get in the car.

Fuck him.

I want to grab her and carry her over to our car and buckle her into the
back seat and pop the trunk and take out the tire iron and crush his
crooked fucking teeth in.

Relax, Glenn. BreatheBreatheBreathe.

I have no good reason to hate this man but there's something familiar
about him. I can smell the booze on his breath and the stench of his
sweaty hair against my face.

BreatheBreatheBreathe.

I breathe slowly, deliberately as I watch Lila walk away.

Yet another moment in a lifetime of moments where I can't figure out
what is real and what is the residue of something long-dead inside me.

"Stuie."

I see the top of Lila's head poking up from the back seat of her father's car and my heart sinks into my belly.

I'm sorry.

I hate this feeling even though it's not new and it's not something I can ever predict.

I'm sorry I can't save you, Lila.

I turn and I put my arm around my father's shoulder and he quickly shrugs it off. I'm not sure if it's because he doesn't want the help or if he doesn't want to forgive me yet for polluting his body with all the stress I just caused him.

We walk to the car and I ease him into his seat and I skate over to the driver's side, drop into the seat and lock the doors.

"You're a *little* turned on, right Dad? That was pretty butch of me."

He sighs and he shakes his head and he tells me to *just fucking drive.*

He only curses when he's pissed or desperate or scared and it feels like he's all of these things at once.

I'm not leaving until I erase this mess.

I place my hand on his knee and start moving it up towards his crotch.

He laughs as he tries to push it away.

The treatment has sapped most of his strength and I take full advantage of the fact that it has.

I put my other index finger up to his lips with a *Shhhhhh. Let's not fight.*

He tries to squirm away.

"Stop it, Glenn!"

I yank my hand away, faux offended.

He shakes his head and speaks through a laugh.

"Jesus, Glenn. What's wrong with you?!

I put the car in reverse and I back out of the spot without breaking eye contact with him. He won't look at me but he senses my stare.

He laughs and tells me to keep my eyes on the rearview.

Thud.

Shit.

I've hit an older white Taurus parked in the row across from us.

He wipes his mouth with a handful of ratty McDonalds napkins and mumbles.

"How bad is it?"

I get out and I walk over and I see the Taurus is undamaged.

Our car now has a fist-sized dent in the right bumper.

I get back in and I start driving.

"Their car's *fine*."

"What about *mine*?"

"Shhhhhh … you're not as pretty when you're upset."

We laugh because it's all we have.

My dent is something we can fix.

massachusetts turnpike, half hour later

We drive the anesthetic treadmill of identical roads and freeways back to my father's house in silence. The wipers squeak out a grating score as I brace myself for the inevitable lecture.

Throat clear.

Here we go.

His voice is airy and weak.

"What the hell was that all about back there, Stu?"

"Really? You know I don't do well with bullies, Pop."

"Bully? Ya ever think that maybe he's just a father who's stressed and worried about his daughter? Someday you'll see how hard it is to see your kid suffer."

I know a kind of *worrying about your kid* he'll never know.

Jen went into labor in the middle of my first round of chemotherapy and my whole fucking world turned to vaseline the minute I got the call at the hospital.

It was the start of a month-long day full of sound and smell and color that disintegrated in my hands as I tried to stay tethered to a reality I was nowhere close to accepting. A reality of holding my own child, a child I would never know, a child I would never be able to protect from the predators who roam this planet unchecked and unpunished.

Hours and hours of Jen moaning and pushing and crying and screaming. Hours of melted memory for both of us that I can no longer distinguish from the truth of that day.

The day I became a father.
The day my father became a grandfather.
The day my son started losing both.

"I actually *do* know what it's like, Pop. It's just that—"
My phone starts to buzz and hop in the cup holder.
I take my eyes off the road and I get a quick glimpse of the screen.
Speak of the devil.
"Want me to get it, Stu?"
"Just put her on speaker."
The snow is falling heavier now, sudden patches of wet gauze are trying to
bury our windshield and hide the road ahead.
Danny is wailing away behind Jen's pleading run-ons.
"Sorry to interrupt you guys, I'm having a really hard time getting your
son to sleep, he won't stop screaming, I'm starting to lo—"
"Did you try warm milk?"
Shit. Shut up, Dad.
"Oh! I hadn't tried that, Mel. That's a great idea. What do you suggest I—"
I jump in and I attempt to cut the right colored wire on this invisible
time bomb.
"—Sorry, Jen. I think the cancer's spread to the old man's brain."
She lets out an annoyed exhale.
"It's fine. When are you coming home, Glenn?"
"First train in the morning."
The wipers are firing away at top speed and it's hard to distinguish
the screech of the rubber from Danny's screams.
The phone screen goes black.
Silence.
"Did she just hang up, Stu?"
Of course she hung up.
"Yeah. I think she's just over it right now, Pop."
"Seriously? It's a *baby*, not terminal cancer."
I laugh, tell him it's worse, tell him at least cancer has naps.
The snow slows as we exit the turnpike and my stomach starts to churn
when I think about Jen and Danny alone in our tiny studio apartment
back home in Manhattan.
She's right.
I should be home with them. Time is all I have and I'm not sure I'm
spending it well.

My father breaks the silence.

"Despite the Rambo shit with her dad, you were so good with that little girl back there, Stuie. It made me think you're gonna be a really great father once you make it through all of this."

I want to remind him that I may not make it through all of this, that even if I'm lucky enough to get more time, it likely won't be much. Instead, I fiddle with the dashboard knobs and bite the inside of my cheek to keep the tears from coming because I know if I open my mouth to speak, I'll fall apart.

"What was that little girl's name again?"

I speak through a bubble in the back of my throat.

"Lila."

"I love that. I think it means *night* in Hebrew."

I love that.

I ease my foot off the gas and I weave my way through the narrow snow-covered streets and I keep my eyes fixed on the blackening sky and I respond only in smiles and nods.

Another sun is gone.

my father's house, fifteen minutes later

We pull into the driveway and I purposely edge the car into a snowbank as if I'm just learning how to drive.

He's annoyed. I inch it a little further into the snow until we can hear the bumper crunch.

"Something's very wrong with you, Glenn."

I get out and I help my father climb the frozen porch steps and I open the storm door and ease him into the chair at the head of the kitchen table.

The house is warm and quiet and safe and the smell of a home-cooked meal feels like a hug we both need.

I breathe in, hold it all deep inside my chest, breathe out.

My stepmother Andrea dips her head into the room and suggests we move to the living room so we'll be more comfortable while she finishes cooking dinner.

I love her.

She's been caring for him 24-hours a day since he got his diagnosis, and she's been kind enough to melt into the walls like a ghost whenever I'm here so that he and I can have the time and space to be alone together for whatever time we have left.

"That's a good idea. Let's do that, Pop."

My father tents his fingers against the kitchen table and slowly pushes himself to his feet.

The sight makes my eyes well up.

Fifty-seven.

Fifty-seven is too fucking young to move this way.

I walk him to the living room and help him into his recliner.

The room is small and beige and warm and the air is both septic and antiseptic at once. Breath and rubbing alcohol and talc and ointment and dead skin.

He sits and he stares absently at the television as his cracked mustard-soled feet wave back and forth like they're attached to someone else's body, living someone else's day.

We sit and we don't talk.

We don't talk about today's appointment.

We don't talk about any appointments.

We don't talk about treatment or tests or medications.

We don't talk about odds or plans or what-ifs.

We don't talk.

We don't talk until he is fast asleep.

I walk to the cabinet next to the TV and I run my finger across the spines of neatly stacked VHS cassettes. Each is labeled with my father's unmistakable chicken scratch. I stop on one labeled 'Summer Fun', dated 1976. The year I turned six. The year before *Summer Not Fun*.

I slip it into the VCR and I fall back onto the couch and I wait for the video tracking to unscramble these time-bleached images I don't recognize.

Andrea walks in, whispers *dinner in ten minutes*, spots the confusion on my face.

"Oh, *that*. He had a bunch of old film converted to video a few weeks ago. It's pretty adorable."

The scrambled screen settles into place. A long strip across the top of the footage is distorted, angled away like the flattened binding of an old photo album.

I'm mesmerized by this blind spot in my memory.

The lawn in front of our first house in New York.

I'm sitting in a faded blue kiddy pool, legs stretched out in front of me, my body tiny and L-shaped, slapping the water like bongos, my older brother Nate diving into frame, tongue out, belly-flopping most of the water onto the sunburnt grass, both of us laughing like we thought we'd live in that moment forever.

The camera zooms in on my face and I wave.

My fingers bend at the tips from the distortion at the top of the screen, my chestnut eyes are big and soft and unbroken in a way I don't recognize. A way they would never look again just a year later.

My father wakes up and speaks like he was never asleep.

"Look at that face."

His eyes are wide open and self-satisfied.

"You used to be such a happy kid, Stuie. What happened?"

I know he's joking, but it's a question I wouldn't mind answering.

"I don't know exactly, Pop. It *could* be that I'm dying. Or that I'll never get to see my *own* son do this stuff. Or maybe—"

"Oh, here we go … "

"—or maybe it's because my father asked God to give him my cancer and now *he's* dying too. Or maybe it—"

"Don't get dramatic, Glenn. You lost your joyful spirit a long time ago."

He laughs. I don't.

Instead, I hold a tiny funeral in my head for all the old deaths those words unearth. The death of trust. The death of truth. The death of safety. And maybe the death of secrets, the only death I'm actively trying to speed up.

Like the cancer coursing through my blood right now, I know it has to be exposed and destroyed if I'm ever going to feel truly free. And I want to feel free.

On the screen, my mother comes into frame and starts to towel off my hair. Her brow is furrowed and her lips are slack and pale and her long brown hair frames her chestnut eyes, dulled with a different kind of broken I now see in my own.

I speak.

"I bet if this thing had sound, we'd know why Mom looks so miserable."

He straightens himself in his recliner.

"What's that supposed to mean?"

I laugh, tell him *don't get dramatic, Dad.*

He sighs, shakes his head.

"Forever that Easter Basket kid, Stuie."

I know what he means by this and I know he means it in a loving way, but it kills me every time he brings it up.

"It's true. You've always been *way* too sensitive, Glenn."

"Says the father with the thin skin and short fuse."

"Don't try to make it about me, asshole."

"I rest my case, Dad."

My father has the biggest, sweetest heart that is almost impossible to reach without getting ripped apart.

He is cotton candy wrapped in barbed wire.

The day he's referring to is the first Easter I remember, my first death at the hand of self-sacrifice.

My mother had been up late the previous night hiding eggs for my brother and me to hunt come morning. Nate had already taken on the loving older-brother job of telling me there *was* no Easter Bunny, that the Easter Bunny was actually Mom and that he would punch me in my *stupid ass-face* if I tattled.

I was five years old. Nate was eight. Always a class act.

The next morning, the four of us stood in the living room admiring the Easter Bunny's handiwork. Mom in her zippered quilted pink housecoat, Dad shirtless and obscenely hairy in a pair of blue silk running shorts, Nate impatiently swaying back and forth in his NY Islanders pajamas, and me, clutching an empty wicker basket against my urine-soaked NY Jets pajamas.

It was a sight to behold: hundreds of foil-wrapped chocolate eggs scattered across every visible surface in the room: the tops of couch cushions, across the coffee table, along the bookcases, all over the rug in the middle of the floor. Not a single one that would qualify as *hidden*.

My heart broke as soon as I saw the sea of painfully conspicuous eggs.

I knew at that moment my job was to protect my mom's feelings. She had clearly spent a lot of time setting this up and I wasn't going to let her down or let her feel like she had failed to make this morning special.

I won't make you sad, Mom.

I set off lifting up cushions, *nope*, moving throw pillows, *nope*, reaching my hand under the couch, *nothing*.

I won't hurt your feelings.

I wandered around the living room pretending I couldn't find a single egg.

Nate followed behind me like a shadow at high noon, scooping up every egg that I "missed" until his own basket was overflowing and spilling out onto the floor.

An hour later, alone upstairs in our bedroom, with his mouth packed tight and dripping with chocolate, Nate let me in on another secret: "Mom and Dad said you might be retarded."

My dad is laughing hard now.

"I hate that story, Pop."

He speaks through his laughter.

"Me too, Stuie. But it sums up both of you so well. You, the delicate orchid, and your brother the cast iron asshole."

I want to end this fun reminiscing session and I want us to stop wasting time, but he's still going.

"Those eggs were *everywhere*. You just walked right past *all of them* like a little white Stevie Wonder."

"I saw every single one of them, Pop. I just didn't want to hurt Mom's feelings."

"You were five years old! No kid that age thinks that way."

"*I* did."

"That's very sweet. And very sad."

I still think that way, Dad.

"Well, I'm glad you figured out that you can't protect people from the truth."

I did figure that out but I don't know how to stop trying.

"We were your parents. You didn't have to protect us. It was our job to protect *you*."

But you didn't.

"Dad?"

"What?"

"Why the hell were we even celebrating Easter, anyway?"

"Your mom thought it would be fun."

"Fun? It ended with you at the top of the stairs screaming, 'Why are we even doing this! We're JEWS!'"

"Well, it's true!"

Andrea interrupts.

"Dinner's ready, guys."

Thank God.

I help my father out of his recliner and I walk him to the kitchen and over to his chair at the head of the table.

Everything is bubbling and alive and steam is billowing up into the tin pendant lamp.

It's all here. *Normal people food.*

Salty, buttery, greasy, nutty, tangy, creamy, sweet.

The flavors that have all been replaced by the cruel fuck-you chemo taste of rusted metal. I breathe it all in, hold it in my lungs for as long as I can, breathe out. *Alive.* Breathe in, hold, breathe out. *We're alive.*

My eleven-year-old half-sister, Julia, runs in, tousles my father's hair like they're opposite ages, flops into her chair. Her enormous translucent green eyes are wide and wet and blissfully unaware of the gravity of the invisible clock counting down from the sky above this house. A muffled tick through a cage of storm clouds.

She knows he's sick. She just doesn't know how sick.

I'm not hungry and he's not hungry, but we eat anyway. We eat because in this moment it feels like the only way to push back against the night. Sweet and warm and safe, even if it's not.

We eat in silence as I watch the trees outside the window slap the side of the house with each new wind gust. Julia says *that's such a scary sound* and I laugh because I want to be scared by simple things again.

my father's living room, one hour later

I lean over and I turn off the lamp and I watch the room go black. The shadows and angles of my father's face change with the fluttering glow of the TV screen. I am hypnotized by the differences in his face with each light shift: older, younger, exhausted, peaceful, angry, wrinkled, worried. Some that break my heart, some that calm it.

His eyes open slowly and he looks around the room as if he's trying to figure out where he is. I speak.

"Let's get you upstairs to bed, Pop."

He keeps his eyes closed and moans as I continue.

"Okay. Well, I have to head back home in the morning—"

He opens his eyes, suddenly more awake.

"—so you can either stay down here and I can make up a bed for you or we can head upstairs. It's your call."

"Upstairs."

"Okay, Pop. Let's get you to bed then."

He swings his legs off the ottoman and I help him to his feet and we make our way upstairs and I do my best to help him navigate each step. He refuses the help this time and I understand. Help feels like the beginning of helpless.

We get to the top of the stairs and he walks into the bathroom and he lowers his sweatpants, sits on the toilet, rubs his face and starts to pee.

"You always pee sitting down, Dad?"

"Honestly I don't know why *anyone* pees standing up."

"You're a complex man, Pop."

"It's smart, Stuie. Think about it. If you and your brother had peed sitting

31

down, Mom and I wouldn't have spent so many hours cleaning piss out of the potpourri dish and the heating vent and off the wallpaper."

I laugh.

"Why's that funny? It's true."

"I don't think you ever cleaned a thing in your life, Dad. Never mind teen piss off a ceiling."

I hear a rumble in the bowl.

"See, Stu? If you suddenly get news from the South, you're ready."

I walk to the sink, grab a book of matches, toss it onto his lap, shut the door as he yells.

"You're gonna miss the best part, Stuie!"

"I really can't believe you have a Ph.D."

He ignores my comment and keeps yelling.

"Turn on the VCR. There's a whole season of *Studs* already in there."

I walk into the bedroom and I yell back.

"*Studs?* You're an adult male!"

I don't want to watch *Studs* or any other show.

I walk over and I sit on the edge of his bed and I stare at the reflection of the lamp against the empty TV screen and I pretend the bowed-out yellowwhite glow is another sunrise we'll both get to see.

day 2

The sun rises on our first morning and the trees are still trying to run away. I was hoping I would wake up to something different, something like the pictures in the brochure: the *crystal clear streams*, the *rolling wildflower fields*, the *bright white sun*, kids smiling like they aren't scared I hear sloshing as Corey wakes up and whispers.

"Glenn?"

I feel myself slosh as I poke my head over the side of the mattress.

Last night in the far stall of the boys' bathroom, Corey gave me one of his special pairs of underpants and told me to wear them when I slept. I held them up and I thanked him and I squeezed into the upside-down-shower-cap-with-tight-elastic-leg-holes thing and I pulled my pajama bottoms up over them. As we crinkle-walked back to the bunk, he told me they were the same rubber shorts the guys in underwater demolition teams wore when they were blowing up enemy ships, "These things can hold up to a year of grownup pee in them." I was excited because I knew that meant it was probably two years of kid pee.

Now he's whispering my name again as he pops out of his bunk. His special underpants are filled to the brim with urine and it looks like he's wearing a small inner tube under his pajamas.

He pulls down his pants, points at them and whispers.

"Check it out, Glenn. No drips."

I look down at my own crotch and see that I've got a full tank too.

Whoa!

I look at him in awe. His hands are now on his hips as he stands in the middle of the cabin, hula dancing the clear yellow tide back and forth across his crotch.

He laughs as he whisper-yells.

"It's a penis fishbowl!"

He shakes and he jiggles and I start to laugh so hard I can hardly catch my breath. My body is shaking and my own fishbowl is bouncing and I look at the trees outside the window and they look like they are standing straight toward the sky for the first time since I got here.

I want to live in this moment forever. I am not alone and I am not afraid.

I am learning what a moment is and what a moment means and why moments can make a person happy forever if those moments never end.

A thunderclap shoots across the room and hits Corey's back the exact moment it hits my chest.

Randy.

I can feel his voice knock the wind out of us.

Dark and cold and hard.

"What the fuck are you two doing?!"

He stands in the doorway that separates all of us from his private sleeping area as the vein in his neck throbs like a rope in a game of tug of war.

The other kids are awake and confused and silent and they look pinned against the wall.

Silence.

Thunderclap.

"What the *fuck* are you two doing!"

Corey pulls his pajama bottoms back up and slosh-runs to our bunk and buries himself under his blanket.

I feel like the silence in here can be heard in heaven.

We all stare at Randy's shirtless body as it tightens and loosens like one of those crazy racehorses waiting for the starter gun.

Owen, the bucktoothed blond boy in the bunk at the opposite end of the cabin speaks without any sense of what all of us are feeling and seeing.

"Randy?"

We all stop breathing. Randy turns his head like an owl and speaks through his teeth.

"What, Owen?"

Owen is deaf to the thunder.

"When's breakfast?"

Randy points, tells him to get off the bunk.

He orders Owen to stand in the middle of the room and then orders Corey to do the same.

There is a poison in the air that I've never tasted before and I close my eyes and I pray to a god I don't even know is real or not.

I start to cry.

StopStopStop.

Thunderclap.

"Glenn!"

I pretend I'm asleep even though I am shaking like Jell-O.

"Glenn!"

Corey calls out to reassure me.

"Open your eyes, Glenn. It's okay."

I open my eyes and I turn to face them. Corey and Owen stand on either side of Randy like they're glued to his giant legs. Through my tears, they look like a hand holding up the middle finger.

Randy orders Owen to pull down Corey's pajama pants and makes Corey turn in a circle so all the other boys can see 'what was so funny.'

Corey holds back tears as he turns and Randy takes a slow lap around the cabin and speaks to all of us like he's an army general and we're a group of captured enemies.

"If *any* of you think it's funny to piss your fucking bed like babies, you're wrong. You're not babies. You're men. And men know how to control their bodies—"

He points to Corey.

"—and now Owen is going to clean up the baby's mess."

He walks over to Corey, gets behind him and yanks his rubber underwear down to his ankles. The urine hits the floor with a bang, like it was dropped from a skyscraper.

Corey's face turns red and his tears come even though he stands as still as concrete.

Randy grabs the green plastic bucket from the corner of the room, tosses it at Owen's feet, yells.

"All of you! Help Owen clean up the baby's piss."

He walks over and puts his finger on Corey's forehead and continues.

"And *baby* will stand right fucking here so everyone can look at baby's broken dick."

I want this moment to end. I am alone and I am afraid. I am learning what a moment is and what a moment means and why moments can make a person sad forever if those moments never end.

back seat of a taxi, the next morning

The sky is still black when I take a cab from my dad's house to the
train station. I can't take my eyes off the rearview mirror. I'm lulled
by the driver's frozen gray eyes brightening and dimming to the
rhythm of passing headlights like tiny sad moons waxing and waning,
completely unnoticed.
Don't be sad. I see you.
We pull into the station parking lot and I fold a twenty-dollar bill and
stuff it through the partition window and I say thank you, *thank you for
getting me here safely.*
I grab my backpack, shimmy across the back seat and make my way over
to the platform to follow the woolen herd onto the train.
I find a seat and I fall into it with all my weight and I get ready to watch
the graygreen blur of Massachusetts on rewind through the window.
I'm going home.
I take out my phone and I call my father, a sad attempt to stay grounded
in both of my dying worlds.
"Stuie?"
"Hey, Pop."
"What's up?"
"Just wanted to hear your voice."
"Mission accomplished, Stuie. How 'bout you get some sleep instead of
talking to me. You've got a long train ride."
"I will. Just have to make a couple calls to square things away
for tomorrow."

"Chemo day?"

"Visiting day."

"What?"

"Visiting day."

"I heard you. You *still* doing those fucking patient visits?"

I started a nonprofit organization called Best Medicine that brings comedians to perform in the living rooms of homebound AIDS and cancer patients in the final weeks of their lives. We bring in three comedians, an actor playing a waiter, an actor playing a heckler and we set up a comedy club in people's living rooms. *Real* comedians, not ones that make the patients look forward to death. Ironically, I started it two years ago, way before I was diagnosed with cancer and given my own death sentence. Tomorrow, I'm going by myself to visit Chris, one of the first patients we did a show for, and now one of my closest friends.

"Stuie. You've gotta focus on your *own* health and your *own* life. C'mon…"

"You know it *is* possible to do both, Dad."

I can feel the anger in his voice.

"No. It's not. You don't have to save the whole world. Especially if it's at your own expense."

Isn't that what you do for a living, Dad?

"That's where you and I differ, Pop."

"That's where you and *everyone on earth* differs, Glenn."

I've always been like this, though: lowest on my own priority list. Mostly because I know I'll be okay. I'll always be okay. It's something I learned a long time ago.

Of course, it hasn't stopped everyone in my life from offering a different theory for why I'm like this:

Low self-esteem. Lack of boundaries. Codependency.

I get it. And I always have. But the two aren't mutually exclusive.

Just because I give everything doesn't mean it all gets taken away.

"I'm not trying to be a fucking hero, Dad."

"I know you're not, but you've gotta take care of yourself and your family."

"I hear you. I really do."

"I don't think you do. You spent an *hour* yesterday telling me how much you miss Jen and Danny and how desperate you were to see them. And now you're telling me that you're spending part of tomorrow visiting a terminally ill AIDS patient? What about your wife? What about your son?"

His words send a wave of lost time through my body.

I let it come in a way that feels almost real, like I'm healthy again, like I'm not free-falling through the helplessness of being unable to control what happens to my body.

I let the memories come.

Nine years with Jen, nine years all at once.

The day we met. That brutally hot Arizona day, my nineteen years to her twenty-two. The glow of the sunset like red wine over tangerine sherbet outside the window behind us as we sat together on that grease-stained couch in my tiny apartment, talking for hours. Her parents divorced, her father in California, her mother dead. Her correcting me when I ask her how long ago it was that her mother passed away, insisting I use the word *dead* instead of softening reality with words like *deceased, passed-on, passed-away*, insisting I never sugarcoat the horrible. The rule I broke when I chose not to tell her about my cancer until after Danny was born. I thought I was protecting her.

I was wrong and she was right.

From the day we met, she said *never sugarcoat the horrible* and I didn't listen and the cost is already starting to feel too big.

Proof being that I'm breathing her, smelling her, feeling her right now through these fragments of memory, instead of feeling her in reality, in the seat next to me, her head on my shoulder, Danny between us, looking up at us with those beautiful brown eyes spread soft like chocolate left in the sun, looking up at *us*, his parents, unified in this shitty truth, in this fight to keep his father, her husband, alive and vertical.

"Dad, listen—"

"And what about *me*?"

He's right.

Time is all I've got and I'm not using it well.

"I'm doing my best to take care of *all of you*, Pop."

"I don't need you to take care of me. Just don't waste your time taking care of everyone but yourself. Know what I mean?"

"Then maybe you should quit your whining and let me fucking sleep, Dad."

He laughs.

"Say goodnight, Gracie."

"Goodnight, Gracie."

I *do* know what he means. I just know it won't change my behavior.
The dull hiss of the fuse behind me gets sharper every day and I can't
stop this urge to cling to all the strangers whose time is also on fire.
I don't know if hanging onto them and trying to save them is my way of
trying to put myself onto the other side of this inevitability, but I have no
interest in stopping.
There's a loneliness to dying that can only be healed by strangers, the
people who don't know exactly what they're about to lose.
I put my legs up on the seat across from me, close my eyes and fall asleep
knowing full well that sleep is just a theft of time.

midtown manhattan, four hours later

My eyes open just as the train is pulling into Penn Station.
I bundle up and follow the herd up the escalator and out onto the street.
The air outside is sour with exhaust and urine and cooked meat and the
sun is high and white like a bleach stain on a denim sky. I love this city.
I love this behemoth, this glass and concrete forest that's somehow less
dangerous than a natural one.
I walk in the opposite direction of my apartment.
If I never go home, then I never have to face the things I don't have. I
never have to face the imaginary things I pretend to love. I never have to
face all the other deaths, all the other goodbyes. I never have to face the
son I don't have and the wife I don't have. The *illusions*.
They're all just illusions and I'm only obligated to give imaginary things
what imaginary things deserve: nothing.
Imaginary things don't need or deserve real things.
I am single and healthy and young and no one deserves or needs anything
from me.
I have a wife and a son and I am dying and they need and deserve
everything from me.
I am single and healthy and young and no one deserves or needs anything
from me.
I am a young, healthy twenty-eight-year-old and I am single and free
of responsibility. I have a life without restrictions, a blue-sky life, a life
without history or baggage, a life where the sun is always out, where the
sun is real and warm and safe, where the sun is not a lie.
I cinch my jacket up to my neck and I walk and I keep track of every

window I pass.

Shoe store, café, bakery, showroom, pub, bar, bodega, bar.

A different kind of counting.

Pizzeria, nightclub, restaurant, bar, electronics store, bar.

Bar. This bar.

The kind of bar where you can get a drink at 10 a.m.

I stop, shade my eyes, see that the front doors are propped open with metal buckets of sand.

I lean my head into the room and I inhale the stale air, the stale air of last night, the stale air of all last nights.

Cigarettes and cheap cologne and puke and piss and a dim pulse of shitty techno music.

A mousy-faced waitress in a white tuxedo shirt is the only other person in the place.

She looks up from her seat at the bar, sees me, nudges her glasses back against her smiling eyes, motions to a long row of empty black velvet booths like a game show spokesmodel.

"World's your oyster."

I walk to the booth furthest from the front doors and I flop down onto the bench and I fold my hands in front of me on the table like I'm waiting to start a job interview.

What the fuck are you doing here, Glenn? Go home. Jen needs you. Danny needs you. Go home.

I order a pint of Guinness, chug it down, order another, chug it down even faster. I'm not a drinker and I get the feeling I'm not supposed to drink but I don't remember why.

You're sick. You're dying.

I cup my hands around the next sweaty pint and I stare out the front door and I watch the shadow of this building swallow the one across the street. An ocean of time ebbing and flowing with nothing ahead of me and nothing behind me, people coming in an out of the double glass doors in waves.

I am numb and soft and lost and my body feels like cotton.

How many pints is this?

I don't remember what number this is. I never counted them. I count everything, but I never counted these pints.

How long have I been here?

The room is suddenly loud, the tables full, the booths packed. The sky is turning black and no one has asked me to leave.

I sit and I watch everyone talk and laugh and yell and drink and it all makes me angry, beyond angry.

Look at these people. They're not dying and they're not running away from dying. They don't have secrets or pain or fear. They have perfect lives and I fucking hate them for it. All of them.

I scan the crowd through the crosshairs of my envy.

A couple talking to a single girl about how magical it feels to be married: *Fuck off.*

Three guys soaked in cologne talking about tits and ass and fucking and fighting: *Fuck you, fuck you, and fuck you.*

A clown-bald man with an enormous gut trying to impress a young emo girl with his bullshit stories about adventures he's never been on with people he's never known: *Fuuuuuck you.*

A shitty little white boy who just dropped three n-bombs trying to convince the two black guys he's with that he's not who he really is: a rich asshole from Long Island with lawyer parents and a trust fund: *Fuck the fuck off.*

A pregnant woman parading around rubbing her belly as if she invented pregnancy: *Fuck you and a half.*

An arsenal of fucks in my brain is chambered and unloading in furious blasts: *Fuck you. And fuck you. Fuck you and you and you.*

Go home, Glenn.

I am numb and soft and lost.

I am far away.

"Anyone sitting here?"

A voice.

Soft and warm and free.

The sound pulls me from my stupor.

The voice belongs to a woman several years older than me. Perfect ivory skin, a waterfall of long red curls, wide emerald eyes, a toothy smile painted yellow by the light of the flickering candle.

I love her. She is all I want and she is all I need.

"No ma'am."

Ma'am? What the fuck, Glenn?

She smiles, sits, extends her hand.

"Maggie."

Fake name fake name fake name.

"Glenn."

Fuck.

I'm twenty-eight years old and I've never been on a date. A formal date, a blind date, a lunch date, a dinner date, a meet-for-drinks date. I've never spent hours alone at a bar and I've never made small talk with a stranger. I've never done most of the things normal people do.

"You expecting someone, Glenn?"

"Just me, myself and I."

'Me, myself and I?' What are you, ten years old?

"You sure you have room for a fourth in there?"

What?

"You're really beautiful."

Smooth, Glenn.

She smiles, furrows her brow slightly, flips a strip of hair up over her head and says thank you in a way that tells me she hears those words a lot.

Jen does the same hair-flipping thing and it always melts me.

Who's Jen?

I feel far away.

"You look like a stoplight."

Her smile disappears.

"I'm sorry, what?"

"You look like a stoplight. Red hair, green eyes, yellow teeth."

Silence.

Okay, Glenn. No more talking.

"Stoplights are beautiful though—"

Stop talking.

"—bright and shiny and colorful. They make people stop. And sometimes they get people to speed up even if they're supposed to be slowing down. The yellow part. You know how sometimes—"

She grabs her glass, stands, straightens a wrinkle from her dress, forces a smile.

"It was nice meeting you, Glenn."

"Waitwait, don't go."

Don't leave me alone.

"I can say *not* retarded things, too."

I don't know why or how this broken stupid sentence keeps her from leaving but it does. She sits back down, tells me to start over, tells me to stop at *you're beautiful* this time.

Her quiet act of clemency fills me with so much joy.

It keeps me suspended in this new space inside my head where I am alive and I am healthy and I am free.

"Okay, Maggie. Tell me about *you*. I'll shut up this time."

She chuckles, sets her hand on mine, looks into my eyes, tells me she's
a photographer for a famous magazine, tells me she's bounced between
terrible relationships over the past several years, tells me she just wants
to fall in love now, start a family, move someplace quiet, laugh every day,
cook every night, maybe write a book, maybe learn an instrument.

"What about karate?"

"What?"

"What about karate? Do you want to learn—"

"Yeah, I heard you. What does that have to do with anything
I'm saying?"

Tuxedo walks up to the table, slides a fresh pint into my cupped hands,
takes away the empty one.

"You just have so many cool plans for your life and I was just wondering if
karate was in there."

"You're joking, right?"

Not really.

"Yes. I am joking."

You said that like a fucking robot.

She asks me if I want to leave, asks me if I want to walk her uptown, asks
me if I want to go back to her apartment.

Sex? Does she want sex? I don't want sex.

I don't want sex. I want to hold her and kiss her and fall asleep with
her and wake up with her. I don't want Maggie for sex, I want her for
love. I want to feel loved. Safe and quiet and worry-free. I want to feel the
kind of love that fills you with relief that the sadness and loneliness and
darkness are over. The same kind of relief I felt when my dad picked me
up after twenty-four days at camp, twenty-four days that felt like twenty-
four years.

I want that relief.

She smiles, grabs my hand, tells me to pay the tab while she uses the
restroom. I pay and I stand and I wait.

I'm happy.

I wait.

She walks back across the room, slips her hand in mine, leads me outside.
The sky is beautiful. It's black and infinite and braided with tin and tissue.
I love it and it feels safe.

I'm happy.

I pull Maggie out of the crowd and over to the side of the building.

"I just gotta call my wife and let her know."

"Your *wife?*"

"Yeah. I just gotta give her the heads-up. Our son's been real fussy lately."

"What the *fuck,* Glenn?"

I don't like that she's being so weird and dramatic. I just want to love her and be loved by her.

"Between my chemo and my dad's chemo, we're all a little sleep deprived. Just gimme a sec."

I lean my head against the building, shield myself from the wind and traffic noise, leave a message on our answering machine.

I'm happy.

I close my phone and turn around. Maggie is gone.

What the fuck?

I'm so confused.

What was her *problem?*

I just wanted to love and be loved. She was all I wanted and she was all I needed.

But now I'm here again, alone.

It feels like another tiny death and I don't know why.

Go home, Glenn.

my apartment lobby, twenty minutes later

I push my way through the revolving glass door, through the blast of
vertical wind that keeps the city's frozen mouth from stealing our heat,
take the elevator up to my floor, steady myself as it bounces to a stop.
My head starts to fog over and my mouth starts to water.
I duck into the freight elevator room, puke into the garbage chute, lean
my back against the wall, slide down to the floor until my head is level
with the metal handle.
A young Asian man in sweatpants and slippers walks in with a bag of
trash. His body stiffens when he sees me. He walks over to the hatch,
drops his bag into it like he's trying to avoid setting off an explosive.
I clear my throat.
"I'm not homeless..."
He says nothing as he tiptoes out. I yell at the closing door.
"People don't usually take an elevator up nineteen floors to be homeless!"
Nothing.
I stand, walk down the hall, open my apartment door, see Jen curled up
on the couch reading a book to Danny. The air in the apartment is warm
and thick with the smell of shampoo and talc and both of them smile
when they see me. I walk over, kiss them, sit down next to Jen and lay
my head on her shoulder.
There's confusion in her voice.
"I thought you said you were going to be home late?"
"What?"
I have no idea what she's talking about.
"The message you just left on the machine? You said you were gonna be

home late."

"What message?"

She pushes my head upright with her shoulder so she can see my face, see if I'm joking.

Oh my God.

I look into her eyes and watch them vibrate with a mix of fear and incredulity. A wave of dread falls through my chest and into my stomach. A shedding glacier.

Fuck.

"I forgot I left you a message."

"What do you mean you *forgot?*"

Her eyes dilate.

Danny senses the panicked air between us and belts out an atomic wail. A guttural broken painful wail. A splintered cry that speaks for all three of us.

"I forgot."

I have no more words because there are no more words. I *did* forget about leaving a message and I *did* forget about the bar and the pints and the woman who looked like a stoplight.

Fuckfuckfuck.

I don't know what's happening and I don't know what is real and what is not. *This has to be a dream, has to be a fucking dream.* People don't just forget hours of their lives. *What is happening.* Today was a dream and now I'm awake and my hand is on Jen's face and I'm thumbing away her tears.

"You smell terrible."

I hear words and they're her words.

"You smell like a bar."

I know she can't be making this up.

"Have you been drinking?" *Yes, yes I have been drinking.*

"You don't drink." *I don't drink.*

"You're not even allowed to drink." *I'm not even allowed to drink.*

"You're scaring me." *I'm scaring me.*

"Where were you?" *I don't know where I was, wait yes I do, I was at a bar with a woman I fell in love with and her name was—*

"What time did your train get in?"—*I don't remember her name.*

"Go lay down." *I think I'm already sleeping.*

"You're scaring me." *I need to sleep.*

"Call your doctor first," *I'll call my doctor first.*

"Should I call 911?" *I don't need an ambulance, right?*

"What time did your train get here?" *I got here this morning and I was at a bar.*

"I can't tell what you're doing." *I'm asleep, I need to sleep.*

"You're scaring me." *I'm scaring me.*

I stumble over to the bed and I lay down fully dressed and fully convinced that both dreams of who I am are equally real.

This is rare but this not new.

I close my eyes and I wait for my sky to go black.

day 3

The sky is black. Tonight is the third sleep and I have stopped drinking water and soda and punch and juice and I am afraid to pee because it burns when I pee and my head feels like a feather in a hurricane when I move and I know I'm not supposed to feel this way.
We are all in our bunks and most of us are quiet.
Randy stands by the light switch. The way he looks at us is louder than a scream.
A couple seconds pass before the cabin is how he wants it to be.
He looks at me and he not-smiles and he grabs his canteen off the shelf and walks it over to me and tells me to drink.
I tilt it just enough to wet my lips and I try to hand it back to him.
His face is red and contorted and he tells me to drink more.
I take a sip to change the shape of his lips.
They don't change, they never change, they never will change, so I drink until there is nothing left, I drink until my belly stings, I drink until I know I am too scared to sleep, I drink until he is happy with my pain.
Why isn't anyone coming to save me?
The lights go out and I am on my back and I am watching the trees behind my head sway upside-down, shaking and scared to fall into the sky. Their arms are dry and brittle and tired and I tell them *it'll be okay* even though I know it's a lie.
I make a pact with them:
I'll stay with you until the sun comes back. I'll stay with you until I can roll onto my belly and make you right side up again. I'll stay with you if you stay with me.

My eyes feel heavy.
Grayblue.
I'm scared to fall asleep.
Grayblue.
I have to stay dry.
Graygray.
I will not fall asleep.
Black.

our bathroom, the next morning

The shower stream is strong and hot against my neck and everything is sharp and bright and colorful. I feel steady, different, grounded, present again. Everything's in its right place.

The pale-yellow tile, the lightning-shaped rust cracks in the tub, the slimy turquoise ring around the drain. Everything's as it's supposed to be, everything's as it's always been.

I sit down in the tub, lean back and let the shower pound my legs. Jen slips her toothbrush back into the paste-caked cup and whispers to me as she walks out the door.

"Don't forget to call Jay and tell him about what happened."

"I won't forget."

I already forgot.

Jay is my doctor. It was his office walls that melted in front of me, his voice that drowned in front of me, his eyes that cried in front of me on that God-sized night three months ago when he gave me the News. *Cancer, everywhere. Three months at best.* We met through Best Medicine when I performed for his patients, for his sick brother, for his dying father. And now he is taking care of *me* as a friend.

I shove the curtain aside, dry my hands on the towel, slip my phone out of my pants pocket.

"G?"

I lower my voice.

"Hey JJ. Sorry it's so early but I promised Jen I'd call you."

"What's that noise, Glenn?"

"Shower."

"You're calling me from the shower?"

"Relax. It's not a hairdryer. I'm only calling because I want to make sure what happened yesterday was normal."

His voice tightens.

"What happened yesterday?"

"Long story."

"Gimme the short version."

"Short version is that when I got back to the city in the morning, I decided I just wanted to spend the day in a bar."

"Okay...and?"

Jen cracks open the bathroom door, leans in, whispers.

"Tell him about the forgetting part."

I nod, give her a dismissive thumbs-up.

"Annnnd I had a few beers and had kind of spotty memory about all of it."

"Why the hell were you drinking, G?"

Jen shoots me a thank-you smile, gently shuts the door again. Steam spirals in her wake like ghosts sent to make sure there are no more interruptions.

"I really don't know. I just want to make sure that I didn't have a stroke or something."

"You didn't have a stroke, G. I'm sure the memory stuff was just your body processing the alcohol along with everything else. Your dad's probably better qualified to answer the psych questions."

"Okay, JJ. That'll help Jen relax. I'll figure out the other shit."

"And no more drinking, G."

"I promise. I don't even drink in real life, Jay."

"I know. But guess what? Yesterday counts as real life."

I tell Jay I love him, close my phone, bend my knees, slide my back flat against the tub and I let the shower pound against my hollow chest.

I don't know exactly what happened yesterday. It's another blind spot in a life with too many others. Another black circle in the center of an old flashlight beam.

downtown apartment building, two hours later

I hit the small finger-stained button on the wall next to the front door and the smoke of my breath tumbles into the early morning air as I wait to be buzzed in.

A sudden, sharp voice I don't recognize from the aluminum box on the wall.

"Cmonin, Glug!"

Despite my father's objections yesterday, I'm about to spend the afternoon with a dying homebound stranger. I don't consider any of the people I've been visiting through Best Medicine to be *strangers*.

The door clicks and I take the elevator to the third floor.

He's right, Glenn. Go home.

I make my way down the long-neglected hallway, the odors shifting with each passing door, an olfactory trip around the globe.

Curry.

Ginger.

Garlic.

Cabbage.

Beef.

Cumin.

Fish.

Dill.

I get to the last door on the right and I knock and the door creaks open and I stick my head in to announce my arrival.

A woman's voice.

"One second."

Paisley. Chris's nurse.

"It's just Glenn. No rush, Paze."

Several seconds of shuffling and a rush of soft footsteps.

She turns the corner smiling and out of breath.

"Sorry, Glenn. I was just helping Chris out of the bath."

Paisley's presence instantly calms me the way it does every week. Everything about her is musical. Her mocha-colored skin, her wide, deep brown eyes, her soft hypnotic smile. She's the fitting final companion for a man I met only a couple years ago but have come to really love.

Jen and Danny are home without you and your dying fucking father is alone.

Chris's voice crawls out from behind the wall.

"Tell Glenn we gave at the office."

I laugh.

"But I need to talk to you about Jehovah and tell you the good news!"

"Is it too late to lock the door, Paze?"

Paisley smiles, grabs my arm, leads me into the living room, insists I sit in her recliner, *best seat in the house.* I thank her, watch Chris wall-crawl across the room and flop down onto the couch. His wet salt-and-pepper hair frames the deep creases in his face and lips. He straightens himself as if his arms and chest are strapped to metal rods and he exhales with a wince as he speaks.

"So…"

I wait for him to catch his breath.

"…you mind talking bummer stuff for a couple minutes, Glenn?"

"For *you*? My favorite patient? I have all the time in the world."

I have none of the time in the world.

He smiles, thanks me. He doesn't know about my health. Weeks ago, I told him that I shaved my head and lost weight for a part in a play, and even though he never called me out on it, I suspect he knows something's up. It's yet another lie, another secret I've convinced myself is protecting someone I love.

"Listen, G. I need to ask you for a favor."

I see his heart in the veins of his neck.

You don't have time to do him a favor.

"And you can certainly say no. It may be a lot to ask."

Say no say no say no.

"Of course! What is it?"

Great job.

"I want you to speak at my funeral—"

My heart settles.

"—and I want you to read some stuff I wrote."

"You want me to read something you wrote at your own funeral?"

"Yeah."

"I sense a *but* coming."

"Nope. No *but.*"

"So why the dramatic wind-up?"

"Because a lot of it'll be really uncomfortable for my family to hear and it'll probably piss my brother and father off. But fuck it. There's a family secret that needs to come out and I just don't think I have the guts to do it myself."

"Chris. You know I *live* to make people uncomfortable."

Paisley lets out a laugh from the kitchen.

"What's so funny about that, Paze?!"

She walks into the room, sets down two cups of tea on a stack of magazines piled up at the end of the coffee table.

"You remember the first thing you ever said to me, Glenn?"

"Uh oh."

"You asked me if I would keep an eye on your stuff while you were in the bathroom."

"And...?"

"And you asked me not to steal any of it."

"What's wrong with that?"

"You said, and I quote, '*I know how you people are.*'"

I put my hand over my heart as if I'm deeply offended.

"I was talking about *nurses.*"

She laughs hard.

"How was *I* supposed to know you were black?"

She speaks through her laughter.

"You're right. I should've told you."

Chris does a dramatic clearing of the throat.

I speak.

"Uh oh, Paisley. Gay Boss doesn't like his Blacks and Jews experiencing mirth."

Paisley laughs hard as she walks into the kitchen, Chris continues.

"You're really willing to do that for me, Glenn?"

"Of course."

"You *sure?*"

"I'm sure."

I'm not sure.

"I just want them to hear the things they wouldn't give me the dignity of listening to before they stopped speaking to me."

Chris came out to his family when he was twenty-two years old and both his father and brother said some vicious things to his face before deciding to never speak to him again. His mother was silent on that day but continued to communicate with him secretly for the past twenty-five years. I know how much pain this has caused him and I love him too much to let all of that go unanswered. I know it's not my place, but I've always felt like his family abandoned him in a forest somewhere and that it's my job to make sure he gets out safe and intact. I want to save him even if it feels like it's too late.

"I'll read whatever the hell you write, Chris. You have my word."

His eyes well up.

"Thank you, G."

"You are *my* Gay and Paisley is *my* Black and I won't let anyone mess with either of you."

"And you're *our* Jew and we won't let anyone mess with you either."

I hear Paisley laugh in the distance and it fills my heart.

The three of us talk and laugh for two more hours.

Two hours I don't have.

Two hours I can't spare.

I don't know why it's so much easier for me to have this level of intimacy with total strangers than it is to have with my own wife, but it doesn't matter now. I'll never have the time to find out. I just spent two hours I don't have.

I stand and I hug them and I kiss them and I tell them I will see them next week.

I say this every week.

I never know when it will eventually become a lie.

my apartment, that night

My eyes open to another black sky, another missing sun.
It's past midnight and I've slept through lunch, dinner, bath time and
story time. Time I should've been awake for. Time I would've been
awake for if I hadn't spent so much of it trying to love a dying stranger.
I stand and I walk to the window to a symphony of weighted breaths, Jen
and Danny fast asleep and trading fours, our cat Murphy curled like a
nautilus in the corner of the couch purring out his own rhythm.
My eyes burn as I stare out the window at the empty grid of Herald
Square, the city still fast asleep.
I sit on the edge of the mattress and I watch Danny basking in the
copper glow of the nightlight and I start to cry when I see him gripping
a strip of Jen's shadow-black hair, the same sleepy waves that have draped
themselves across my chest and calmed my heart for thousands of nights
before Danny was even a thought.
His face is puckered and his legs are twitching like he's trying to kick
away a cloud of moths.
He's afraid to let go.
I put my hand under his feet and for some reason this makes me
stop crying.
I'm afraid to let go.
I lean back against the pillow and I slip my finger into his free hand and
for some reason this makes him stop twitching.
His tiny hand grips my finger and I cry and I stare at the ceiling and I
move small bits of my mouth around with my tongue like lost scraps of

shredded coconut and I swallow each one.

I've lost several layers of my mouth to the poison they've been pumping into my blood for weeks and I just want it to stop falling away. I want to stop swallowing pieces of myself just to try to keep myself intact.

my bed, the next morning

I bolt awake, my phone vibrating on the nightstand.

"Did I wake you up, Stuie?"

"It's fine. I gotta be at work in a couple hours."

I've been working at a commercial printing lab in midtown Manhattan for the last several years, a low-paying job that services the ultra rich of Wall Street and Madison Avenue, a job I love despite its tedium because it's allowed me to do stand-up almost every night for years without having to live out of a refrigerator box. It's a job that pays my rent, a job I am incredibly grateful for, a job that has been beyond generous with allowing me time off not only for my own treatment, but also for time off to be with my father during his.

"Work? You're joking, right?"

"I've gotta work, Dad. Still have to pay bills, ya know?"

"Yeah, but you're—"

"Dying?"

"Sick ... Shoot, hold on Stuie."

I hear the phone drop and I hear him run to the bathroom and vomit.

He moans like I've never heard him moan before.

Long, low, primal. *I should've never left him.*

I watch the clock.

Eight minutes.

I hear a shuffling as he adjusts himself back onto the bed.

"Dad?"

"Sorry Stuie."

He's crying.

I suggest emailing instead and he agrees.

"I'll miss you, Stuie."

"I miss you too."

Wait.

Did he just say "'I'll' miss you?"

Words are forming their own shapes now.

my office, three hours later

I sit at my desk and I fill out the last of the employee evaluation forms
I'm required to complete by the end of the month. This one's for Juan,
the sweet, doughy-faced kid who gave the answer, "my lunch" when I
asked him that idiotic interview question, "What do you think you can
bring to the company?"

He wasn't joking. I hired him on the spot.

My office phone rings, a number I don't recognize.

"This is Glenn."

"Oooh. What are you wearing, Glenn?"

My stepdad, Ron.

I laugh, tell him *just a bowtie and a smile.*

"How you holdin' up, kiddo?"

"As good as can be expected, I guess. I spent most of yesterday with Chris
and Paisley when I probably should've been with home with Jen and
Danny."

"Well, you're in luck 'cause your mother and I just landed and we should
be at your apartment in—"

"—hold on one sec, Ronnie."

A gray-haired man in denim overalls walks past my door carrying a big
piece of Tupperware that's belching out steam like a locomotive engine.
The stink it's giving off is unholy. A sharp, spoiled, sour odor that's
worsened by my chemo-heightened sense of smell.

"Jesus Christ, Bob! Are you eating a fried fuckin' cat dick out there!"

Ron clears his throat, sighs into the phone.

"It's amazing you've managed to stay employed, Glenn."

"Sorry, Ronnie. Seriously, though. What kind of asshole cooks fish in the office microwave?"

He ignores me, continues.

"Well, I'm *glad* you went to see Chris yesterday—I actually think it helps you stay grounded. God knows you don't do so well when you're left alone with that messy head of yours."

Bob walks into my office, parades his steaming fish head around the room as he gives me the finger.

That's fair.

"I gotta go, Ronnie. I'm supposed to pick up a bunch of new meds I'm gonna have to take from now on. I guess Jay doesn't think the chemo is fun enough on its own."

"Okay, kiddo. Well, try not to kill anyone in the meantime."

I tell him I'll try, tell him I love him, hang up, grab the jackets off the back of my chair and close the door behind me. I pass Bob's desk on my way to the elevator. He looks up from his Tupperware bowl, his glasses completely steamed over. He looks incredibly sad and for some reason it makes me jealous.

outside my office building, five minutes later

I wrap myself in a burrito of gortex and wool and I walk the seven blocks to the pharmacy near my office. I trudge through the oily snowbanks, push past the smoking teens blocking the front door, skate down the wet linoleum floor all the way to the pharmacy counter and get in line behind an elderly woman.

I stare at the naugahyde skin of her neck and I watch her shoulders shake as she pleads to the lab-coated troll behind the counter.

I smell suntan lotion.

Who the fuck is wearing suntan lotion in the middle of winter?

The woman sounds desperate.

"Last month it was only ten dollars and now it's almost a hundred?"

The pharmacist wipes his greasy forehead with the back of his hand, ignores her, motions for me to step to the counter.

I speak.

"It's okay. G'head and help her. I can wait."

He shakes his head in a don't-worry-about-*this*-lunatic way and raises his voice.

"Next in line."

"Finish with her. I'll wait."

He's getting more agitated with each passing second.

"How can I help you, Sir?"

"Start by helping her."

He raises his voice again.

"Sir. Are you dropping off or picking up?"

"Picking up. *After* you help her."

The woman looks at me, inexplicably annoyed that I'm trying to help. She turns back to Lab Coat, speaks with an angrier tone.

"I've been paying $10 for the last two years."

His face now looks like it's been sprayed with wood polish.

He slaps his hand against the counter, wipes his brow with his sleeve and walks to his keyboard.

I interrupt.

"*I'll* pay for her medicine. Just give it to her so she can go."

He ignores me.

My own rage starts to bubble up behind my throat.

"Give her the meds. I said I'll pay."

He bags the pills and hands them to the woman. We both watch in silence as she shuffles toward the door without a thank-you, as if this was always part of the plan.

Fuck.

I have no money.

Credit card. You'll probably be dead before the bill comes.

I hand him my card and he shakes his head and he swipes it through the machine as if he's trying to slice through the counter. He looks up without making eye contact with me and he speaks to the cardboard drop ceiling instead.

"Your last name?"

I stand on my toes and crane my way into his sightline.

"Rockowitz?"

He turns to the bank of identical white drawers behind him, overflowing with amber bottles of all shapes and sizes.

He calls out over his shoulder.

"Name again?"

"Rockowitz."

"First name?"

"Glenn."

He roots around like a blind hog sniffing out a truffle he has no intention of digging up, walks back to the counter, shrugs his shoulders as if he's done everything he can do.

"Nope. Nothing."

I give him the benefit of the doubt, step aside, call Jay.

"JJ, the pharmacy is saying they don't have anything?"

Jay confirms the number and the location and he tells me he called everything in yesterday and that it should all be there.

I step back over to the counter.

"My doctor said he called everything in yesterday. Can you just double-check?"

Lab Coat sighs like he's just finished a ninety-six-hour shift at the bottom of a coalmine.

"Look, Sir, I already looked. Maybe you got the wrong pharmacy."

My heart tightens. The rage surges forward. I know I can only grind my teeth for so long before the storm switch gets flipped.

"Can you please, *please* look again. They're cancer meds. They're not optional."

He makes eye contact for the first time.

"Look, Sir, I checked already."

Sir.

He spits the word out like a slur.

The word ignites the stream of gasoline in my veins. I can see what's coming and I almost step back from it.

"Go. And. Look. Again."

Stop fucking with me.

Just let me go, already.

My thoughts suddenly feel like shingles clinging to the side of a house in the middle of a hurricane.

Is this the motherfucker who's wearing suntan lotion in the middle of winter?

My brain is gone.

Suntan lotion?

He turns, walks back to his computer, ignores me.

FuckfuckfuckstopGlennstopstopstop.

Shingles are flying off the house like dead skin.

Fuckfuckfuck.

I lean over the counter and grab the base of the spinning metal tree of reading glasses.

Stop fucking with me just let me go.

I slam the metal against the Formica until all the glasses fly off.

FuckfuckfuckstopGlennstopstopstop.

Slamming over and over.

Smashingbangingslamming.

I use the empty rack to destroy everything else on the counter and the fluorescent world around me is blurryblurryblurry and his hysterical voice is a dark wave and I am underwater being choked by this force inside me, this force I don't deserve.

I hate this I hate this I fucking hate this.

And even as I flail, there is a tiny part of me that tries to grab that force by the throat and pin its head to the ground so no one has to see this, has to feel this, has to watch this toothless catastrophe.

I'm sorry I'm sorry I'm sorry.

Everything goes black.

pharmacy floor, probably minutes later

I open my eyes to three cops, three too many for an atrophied 148-pound cancer patient. I don't know how long it's been since that dark vigilante force booted me from the driver's seat, but I'm here and I'm sweating and I'm trying to catch up with the movement of my eyes. The silver-haired one speaks with a kind of detachment that makes me feel slightly less insane.

"We need you to calm down, Sir."

Calm down? 'Sir?'

I mumble.

"Yes. I think I'm better now. I think I'm calm."

Lab Coat is yelling and gesturing behind the cops like an angry fruit stand vendor in the wake of a wild Hollywood car chase. The cops look like they've had their fill of him.

Sounds suddenly sharpen and the gel of everything under my skin starts to firm and I feel clear as I speak.

"I'm sorry."

One cop thumbs his belt as he speaks.

"What happened here, Sir?"

I look around and see the hurricane's path drawn in scattered toiletries and reading glasses.

Why are you guys so calm?

"I need my stuff. I'm sick."

That should clear things up, Glenn.

"What stuff?"

"My meds."

They think I'm a junkie.

"I just finished a round of chemo and my doctor has me starting a bunch of new stuff."

Second Cop pipes up.

"My sister's going through the same thing and it's some scary shit."

I exhale in a way I haven't in weeks.

Seen.

"Thank you."

He turns around and yells to Lab Coat.

"Do you have this kid's medicine or not?"

"No! I looked!"

"Well, look again! And look really fuckin' hard this time!"

"I already—"

"Do it!"

Lab Coat turns around, motivated for the first time since I walked in.

He starts flailing through the drawers like a muppet powering through cookie boxes.

Second Cop asks me my name again, turns back to Lab Coat.

"His last name is Rockwoods! Find it!"

Third Cop smiles, points to my shirt.

Shit.

My brother Nate bought me a Stone Cold Steve Austin WWF shirt as a joke and I forgot I was wearing it today.

I look down and see the words *100% Ass Kicker* emblazoned across my boney chest.

"Oh, *that*. Yeah. I don't even watch wrestling."

He smiles.

"Okay, *Ass Kicker*."

I flex my pretzel stick arms.

"Auschwitz Golden Gloves, three years in a row."

No more smile.

Lab Coat casually announces my name as if we'd all been waiting patiently without psychotic incident.

"Rockowitz, Glenn. Your prescriptions are ready."

What the fuck?

Maybe I'm not the only crazy one here.

The cops stick around for a couple minutes after I pay for my poisons and they help me clean up the mess I made.

So simple.
I love these men.
The human being at its best and worst.
I've known both.

day 6

His breath is against my face and it smells like medicine.
I think it broke a part of my brain because I don't remember how
I got here and I don't know how much time has passed since my sky
went black.
I remember colors and smell but not sound.
Plastic, pee, wood, alcohol, suntan lotion, salt, pine trees, dirt, sun. I am
barefoot and shirtless and alone with Randy behind the cabin and we are
standing under the window that has been my periscope since I got here.
I am shivering and I am scared and I am chewing the side of my tongue
and all I can taste is copper.
I don't know if it's copper but it's a penny taste and I want to disappear
but Randy is not laughing and there are no pennies and my feet are
cement and I don't know if I have a tongue anymore.
I don't care. Chewing is all I can do when I can't speak.
I can hear him now and his voice sounds like needles.
"I'll show you."
He points to my crotch.
"Pull those down."
I can hear the other kids running around inside the cabin and I don't
know why none of them are coming to save me.
I hook my thumbs into my waistband and pull my pants and plastic
underwear down to my feet and I feel like I do when I scrape my knee on
the asphalt outside my house. Peeled back and electric.
The kind of open that might never close.
I chew on my tongue as he pulls down his red satin running shorts.

I turn my head away and I look up at my tilted tree friends.
They look like they're trying to run away.
"Glenn!"
My tears are oily on my eyeballs and I won't let them fall because they're
what got me here and I don't want to be here.
"Glenn!"
I can't speak.
He grabs my chin and he makes me look into his eyes.
Big black periods.
"You paying attention? I'm trying to help you."
He lets go of my face and grabs his penis with his giant sandpaper paw
and he squeezes it and pulls it and strokes it and I start to hold my breath.
The smell of his teeth and aftershave and suntan lotion float around my
body like one of those clouds in the cartoons and I try to imagine the
cloud is made of poison gas so that each time he takes a deep breath, I
can pretend it's slowly killing him and soon this will all be over and I will
be safe.
His breaths get deeper and faster as he stares at my naked penis and balls
and legs.
I'm scared and my body feels stuck and my legs feel like they're buried in
the dirt.
All I can do is lean away and I don't even know if I'd ever be able to lean
back far enough to feel not so scared.
The breeze flows through me and the smell of the pine needles calms my
heart and the sun on my back feels like the yellow blanket I put over my
head when I sleep.
It's the smell of the carpet in my brother's room and I miss it.
I try to stay in this place inside my head because it is safe and warm
and invisible.
He is looking right through me and his eyes are watering and I hope
he is crying but I know he's not.
He makes a weird deep sound and he closes his eyes and then he
gets quiet.
I smell his suntan lotion and it burns my nose.
It's supposed to be a nice smell but it's not.
He reaches down and pulls his shorts back up and as he bends over, his
curly hair touches my face.
He whispers into my ear almost as loud as regular talking.
"I'm helping you, Glenn."

I nod to let him know I understand.

I don't understand.

He disappears around the corner and now I feel like those shots my dentist gives me before he puts that drill on my teeth. My gums feel fat and my teeth feel rubbery and I know all the other kids will notice and I don't want them to notice. Everyone will see and they'll say nothing. It'll be a secret everyone can see and people aren't supposed to see secrets. I pull up my pajama bottoms, walk over to my slanty tree friends, touch them and tell them it's okay, tell them it's over.

It's okay.

I understand why you're trying to run.

my apartment building, night

Six hours pass since my shit parade at the pharmacy. Six hours that feel
frantic and glacial all at once. A full sprint on dry sand.

As I make my way down the hallway, I feel a different energy coming
from my apartment door. I look at my phone and I see it's early enough
for Danny to still be awake.

I slip my key in the lock, open the door.

Fuck.

My mom and Ron are here.

Even though I'm happy to see them, I'd already forgotten that they were
coming to visit.

"There he is!"

Ronnie's deep baritone splits the air wide open as he walks over and
wraps his giant arms around my chest. Over his shoulder, I see my
mother standing behind him, smiling and patiently waiting with Danny
asleep in her arms. Ron's enormous belly prevents my arms from making
anything tighter than a loose U-shape so I speak into his shirt.

"SogoodtoseeyouDad."

He pulls me off, grips my shoulders, looks deep into my eyes as the foyer
light over his head turns his silver-blonde hair to a frosted bird's nest. He
mumbles just loud enough for me to hear.

"Ya look good, kiddo."

My heart spreads soft like a burning candle on time-lapse.

Ron doesn't bullshit me.

His words mean what they mean, and if he says I look good, then I can
allow myself to let that seed take root inside me.

"Is that my Glenny?"

My mom wants a turn, her long graying locks pulled back in a loose ponytail revealing her deep chestnut eyes. My eyes, Danny's eyes.

"Hi Ma. I feel terrible that I forgot you guys were flying in today."

She pulls out of the hug.

"How could you forget?!"

Because I'm fucking terrified every minute of every day and I don't have the capacity to process anything in real-time, never mind a day or a week in advance?

"I don't know. I just forgot."

She's annoyed, almost hurt when she speaks.

"Well, we're staying with friends uptown so you don't have to worry about us being in your way."

Are you serious?

Ronnie interrupts when he sees my face.

"Glenn and I will go pick up some dinner. This way you guys can relax and I can take my terminally-ill son for one of his last trips into the real world. We'll probably pick up some hookers too, so don't wait up."

I laugh. He's always been so good at taking a sledgehammer to the ice in a room. Jen shoots me a pleading look that says *don't leave me here alone* and I assure her with my eyes that we won't be long. Ron follows me out into the hallway, shuts the door, puts his arm around me.

"Okay, now tell me how you're *really* doing, kiddo."

I give him the bullet points on our way to the elevator:

The clinical trial I finished a few weeks ago seems to be buying me some time, my dad is getting worse despite the fact that his doctor says things are stable, Jen is struggling, I don't know how to fix the mess I keep perpetuating with my fucked-up behavior, Danny is the only love that feels safe and permanent to me even though he probably doesn't have the capacity to understand who I am or why I matter, Jay continues to lovingly treat my cancer like it was his own and seems determined to save my life for reasons I don't really understand but am incredibly grateful for.

The elevator opens and we sew ourselves into the crowd. He continues our conversation despite the group of strangers now standing between us.

"Did you get to talk to your dad about the Colorado stuff?"

"Colorado stuff?"

"Yeah. The stuff you were debating on telling him ..."

The elevator stops and two more assholes force themselves on, as though there aren't three other elevators in the building.

"You lost me, Ronnie. What are you referring to?"

Ron does TV narration for a living. His voice is deep, booming, God-like.

"The molestation?"

Holy. Shit.

My face floods red as I scramble to save myself.

"Molestation?! I never saw that movie."

The elevator bounces to a stop and the doors open and everyone spills out into the lobby. He extends his arm, motions for me to lead the way.

"Après vous, Mademoiselle."

"You're such a dick."

He laughs, pulls my head toward him, kisses my hair.

"Eh, you'll get over it."

Ronnie is the only one who knows about that summer. A couple years after moving in with us, he confided in me a story of a similar event from his own childhood, claiming that something I casually said over dinner one night set off his Spidey senses. He wanted to give me the space to talk about it, the space to maybe not feel so alone with the weight of my secret. I don't know what would've happened to me in my teen years if he hadn't given me that gift.

The clearest, fullest memory I have from my post-camp life is of the two of us sitting at that small table in the corner of our local Chinese restaurant in Phoenix, vomiting out the vivid details of our shared childhood nightmares. The red paper lanterns shifting quietly each time the air conditioning started up, the twinkle of the ice in my glass as it melted in the silence, a baby banging a spoon against a table in the far corner of the restaurant, the hushed boom of his voice.

"Glenn. Look at me . . . It's over now. It's okay to stop carrying it."

The black and red and orange and gold of that empty restaurant suddenly became an oil painting in a wind tunnel, a thick smudge of color through my tears, an image that would wind up being sharper and clearer than any other image in the years between camp and that moment. Someone was going to help me carry this weight.

We slip out of my apartment building and into the rush of people streaming down 34th Street.

"What were you thinking dinner-wise, Ronnie?"

"No idea."

"Didn't you just tell Mom and Jen that we were gonna pick up food and bring it back?"

"I just wanted to get the hell out of the apartment. And quite frankly, I *really* don't like the woman."

I laugh.

Another sledgehammer to the ice.

my apartment, four hours later

The sun is gone and my mom and Ron are gone and Jen is sleeping and
her porcelain skin is somehow still perfect and intact.

I hold Danny against my chest and I sway back and forth on the 4-foot
dance floor that bridges the bedroom and the living room and I kiss his
silky brown hair, the same color mine was as a boy, over and over and
over, as if I'm trying to cover it and stop it from blackening the way mine
did. As if I'm trying to protect him from all the invisible things I see
hiding in the shadows, poised to pounce.

I find moments like these in the emptiest part of the night—moments
when I have the dumb courage to deny all this is happening—are the
only times I can convince myself that I am not dying, that Danny is not
growing, that Jen is not shouldering the jagged weight of this mess, that
these memories of things I want to keep locked away are just a dream.

I am floating and I am not afraid.

Buzzing.

My heart jumps.

A tiny aqua glow, a dying neon fish.

My phone.

I grab it off the nightstand, silence it, slip out the front door and into the
hallway.

"Pop?"

"Hey Stuie."

He's wheezing.

"You okay, Dad?"

"Yeah. Just a rough night."

"I told you to email me, Pop. Save your voice."

Danny starts to squirm and I kiss his forehead to settle him.

"*Save your voice?* C'mon, Stuie."

"What?"

"You're such a girl."

I laugh.

"My father the shrink, ladies and gentlemen."

A young blond man in pajamas and a raised sleep mask opens the apartment door next to mine and shushes me. He's close enough that I can smell whatever lotion he uses on his face and the smell agitates me. I wince apologetically and I whisper.

"Shoot. Sorry."

He shushes me again and I repeat my whisper.

"So sorry."

He puckers his mouth to shush me again and I interrupt at full volume.

"Alright I don't need a *third* lap on the fucking shushing!"

I hear my father laugh as the guy slips back into his apartment.

"You're such an ass, Stuie. Why're you so angry?"

"Why am *I* so angry? This is coming from a guy who still hasn't forgiven me for leaving the cover off the VCR in 1979."

"Dust *ruins* those machines, jackass. And they were expensive back in those days."

"See? It's an apple-far-from-the-tree thing clearly."

Danny is in such a deep sleep and I can't stop kissing his little fat cheeks.

"Dad, listen. I'll take the train to see you tomorrow."

"That would be great, Stuie."

I tell him I love him but I don't think he hears me.

my father's bedroom, the next day

I take a cab from the train station to my dad's house and I crawl into bed
next to him as he sleeps. The sun falls behind the neighbor's house again
and leaves a bright red laceration across the sky, a wound healed only
by darkness.
He opens his eyes and sees me staring at the sky.
"Beautiful one tonight, huh Pop?"
"All sunsets are beautiful when you're dying, Glenn."
"That's fun."
He chuckles, points to his distended belly.
"Look at this thing, Stuie. What should we name it?"
I know he's trying to deflect his fear the same way I do. I force a laugh
and put my hand on his belly like I'm waiting to feel a tiny kick.
I wish everything felt the way it used to feel. The way it did only a few
months ago. A time when he thought he just had chronic heartburn,
when I thought I was just tired from working too much, when Jen
thought she was just a pregnant wife with a healthy husband, when we
were all just excited for everything ahead of us instead of terrified of it.
It was a kind of unknown that feels so far away now.

I keep thinking about Jen. Her face the moment I walked into our
apartment that night a year ago, the way she stood patiently in our
kitchen trying to tamp down an elated smile, the tentative way her eyes
sparkled as she held up the plastic pregnancy stick, anxiously waiting to
study my reaction when this new reality settled across my face.

"Oh my God."

My only words. She looked crestfallen and elated all at once.

"Is that a *good* 'Oh my God' or a *bad* 'Oh my God,' Glenn?"

Oh my God.

"It's a *good* 'Oh my God!'"

"You sure?"

"Yes!"

Oh my God.

"You should tell your face."

I laughed, pulled her against my chest, kissed her head and swayed to the weird disjointed rhythm of our hummingbird hearts. I was terrified and excited and anxious and lost and grateful. I felt surprised that I felt grateful and I don't know why. I wouldn't find out I was dying for another eight months. I was going to get the chance to be the kind of father who would always protect his kid from whatever came its way. It felt like a kind of infinity only gods get to feel.

Her warm tears seeped into my shirt as I stared at the ceiling light. Her body shook. My body was still.

I watched a small moth flutter between the fluorescent bulb and cracked plastic casing as I mumbled *I love you* into her hair.

Her response was just a vibration against my cheek, but it felt like an *I love you too*. That kind of unknown feels so far away now.

Wake up, Glenn.

My hand is still on my father's belly and I have no idea how long it's been there.

"Stuie? Tumors don't kick. I think ten seconds max is proper etiquette for dad touching."

Ten seconds. Not horrible.

"Sorry, Pop. I've never been good at human contact."

He laughs, mocks my words.

"*Human contact?* Who molested you, Stuie?"

I cringe, force a smile.

"I can't believe you're a shrink, Dad."

He smiles, raises the volume on the TV and closes his eyes.

"Now shut your mouth. Daddy's going to meet Jesus."

I laugh.

A real laugh that's more beautiful than any sunset.

my father's bedroom, two days later

I'm as grateful for this time we've had together as I am shattered for it to
end. I hate leaving him. I hate any kind of leaving.
I inch my way off the bed and I lean back to kiss his forehead as he sleeps
and I walk out of the bedroom and sit down on the floor to write him a
note under the dim light of the hallway.

> *Chemo tomorrow.*
> *Sleep well, Pop.*
> *I love you and I'll call you tomorrow.*
> *P.S. Don't die before I get back.*

Even though the worst part of my treatment—the 'experimental' part
where they injected a radioactive isotope into my blood and kept me
quarantined from all human contact for days, the Hail Mary clinical trial
that was still in its early and most dangerous stages—seems to have had
some success pulling me from the precipice of imminent death, Jay tells
me I still need to inject more chemical lava back into my veins to kill the
cells we don't have the equipment to see.
It's time to light my blood on fire again. It's time to get tired again and
I'm fucking tired of being fucking tired. I'm tired of the trail of fear
that drifts through my brain a hundred times a day telling me not to get
comfortable and I'm tired of the way it makes me question every single
decision I make, whether life-changing or mundane.
I'm tired of the fact that disclaimers are now headlines.
I'm tired of weighing it all equally or not weighing it at all.
I'm tired of feeling that even the smallest choices are an existential

tightrope walk where the crash is a better option than the safety net. I'm tired of believing the lies I've told myself about how life is easier when I handle fear and loneliness alone inside my head.

I'm tired of parsing out what I tell some people and not others.

I'm tired of the lies of omission.

I'm tired of carrying the weight of my secrets and I'm tired of the loneliness they've created.

I'm tired of not being able to control my own body.

I'm tired of other people deciding what to do with my body.

Tomorrow is chemo, a magical kind of misery that I want to be as far away from as possible without losing a single second.

hospital infusion room, manhattan, seven hours later

I feel every second of this. The smell of the chemo room jolts my nose in a new way today. It's sharper, stronger, angrier. Like it's pissed I'm still alive. A nine-volt battery on the tongue.

Half of the infusion chairs are empty and the sight gives me a sudden, deep ache in my bones.

"You okay, Glenn?"

Elizabeth. The sweet, beautiful Black nurse with the deep almond eyes who's run this sad ship since I started coming here.

I shake the fog from my eyes, hug her, kiss her cheek.

"Yeah yeah. I'm good. Sorry, Elizabeth. I'm just surprised to see so many empty chairs."

She walks me to my lucky chair at the far end of the room.

"It's a *good* sign, Glenn. With my job, the fewer customers the better."

She slides the poison dart into my chest and my mouth starts to water and the taste of the memories of all my days here roll over me like a tidal wave. Rust and bile and flowers and melted vinyl. Flavors of defeat. I bite the pitted remnants of my cheek to stop myself from crying.

An older man sitting two chairs down clears his throat and speaks.

"If you think it's bad already, you better buckle up."

I laugh even though I'm not sure he's joking.

"I'm not crying from the chemo …"

I find myself hypnotized by the archipelago of white hair patches scattered across his scalp as I continue.

"… I'm crying because I'm tired."

"Join the club, pal. We're *all* tired."

I've always trusted my gut assessment of people when I first meet them. My friends call it my *deep scan,* and while it may not have been born behind that cabin, it certainly became surgical in its precision that summer. I don't know if this deep scan is a good thing or a bad thing, but it has been an accurate thing.

I introduce myself almost out of habit, "Glenn."

His voice crumbles like old mortar, "Ray Asher."

I don't know why, but I don't like this man.

I don't like this man and I don't trust this man.

I close my eyes and focus on my breathing.

"Hey Glenn … "

Fuck.

His voice feels like pollution. Sticky, heavy, toxic.

I open one eye and give him permission to speak without saying a word. He looks annoyed that I'm not fully engaging him but I already know this kind of guy only speaks in monologues. I am not a fellow patient and I am not a fellow human being. I am an audience. And I suspect everyone in his life has been relegated to the same role.

"This place sucks, Glenn—"

Red flag. Too many times using my name.

"—the nurses don't give a shit about anybody."

He lowers his voice.

"Especially if you're white—"

Bingo.

"—it's almost like we all gotta pay for something shitty someone did a long time ago."

I can tell I'm not the first to get this speech and I can tell it's not the first or second or third time Elizabeth has had to sit through it quietly behind her desk like she's trapped in the back seat of the worst limousine ride in history.

I catch her eye for a second and she smiles at me in a way that tells me to leave it alone.

A whipping motion outside the window catches my eye, a tree shouldering a fierce gust of rain and snapping back without a second thought.

The sight calms me for a second and I draw in a long deep breath.

One two three four five six seven.

"Slavery's over, people. Get over it."

Let it go, Glenn. Let it go.

Eight nine ten eleven twelve.

Elizabeth stands up from behind her desk and comes over to check on my IV. Our eyes meet, and I can tell she's waving the same cautionary flag I'm waving in my head as she speaks.

"How're my guys on *this* side of the room?"

Ray's voice warbles like a child who's been caught stealing.

"We're good over here."

"Good, Ray. What about you, Glenn?"

I smile and I speak with my eyes still closed.

"I just started rooting for my cancer."

infusion room, two hours later

I finish my drip and I sit quietly as Elizabeth untangles the clear
marionette strings from my chest and arms. I lean over and I tell her
I'm willing to lie under oath if she wants to go over there and jack up
the geriatric Grand Wizard with antifreeze. I tell her I'm willing to do it
myself if that sounds safer or more fun.
She laughs way too hard.
"I believe that you actually *would*, Glenn."
"Are you kidding me, Elizabeth? Jail would be a goddamn delight
compared to all this."
A rolling laugh, "Hmm. I don't know about that."
"Elizabeth. Look at me: Three full meals. Lifting weights all day.
Nonstop sex."
"Goodnight, Glenn."
I hug her and thank her and tell her I'll see her next week if I'm still
above ground.
She tells me I will be. She tells me this every time I leave and I've never
believed her.
I want to believe her.
"Goodnight, Elizabeth."
Goodnight, Elizabeth.
I walk through the hospital lobby and I step on the magic rubber carpet
and the glass doors slide open and kick me back into the cold black night.
I walk a few blocks uptown and I realize I don't have the strength to
make it all the way home. The rain has started up again, an icy sideways
rain. I shiver under the awning of a nearby bodega with the other weather

refugees and I take out my phone and I call my dad.

"Stuie?"

"Hey, Pop."

"You calling from Bosnia? It's so loud."

"Just rain."

"Glad you're using electricity in the rain."

Again with this one.

"It's not a hairdryer. And by the way, it's good to hear *your* voice too, Dad."

"You're so sensitive, Stuie. Did you just finish treatment?"

"Yeah. Heading home to see the Governor."

He nicknamed Danny *the Governor* for a reason I don't understand but it makes me laugh.

"How ya feeling?"

"Tired. A little nauseous. But fine."

"Well, get on the subway and get—"

A wave of electricity shoots through my body and everything flickers
redblack
redblack
redblackredblack
and I am freezing and on fire and my skull is firing off whiteyellow bolts of lightning
and then the red is gone
and time is gone
and everything is black.

My brain just did this weird skip thing.

White, black, white.
Like one of my dad's projector trays when it's missing a slide.
Black white black.

And now I'm here and the sky is still black and the trees are flickering
orange from the campfire and I have no idea how long I've been asleep.
I'm afraid to sit up and look around.
I don't want to know what the other kids are doing and I don't want to
know what the lions are doing. I just want to close my eyes again and
wait for the sun to come back.
I lie still and I watch the smoke from my breath float up and disappear
into the cold black sky again.
That hole in the pine tops now looks like charcoal bricks sprinkled with
salt. More stars than I've ever seen in my life.
It looks so beautiful even though I know it's not.
Cricket songs, rustling tree limbs, the crackle of burning wood. I know
these are sounds that are supposed to feel good to people but they don't
feel good to me at all.
It's crazy to think that my dad paid a lot of money for a machine that
makes these same sounds. He uses it in the waiting room of his office so
his patients who are waiting to cry can't hear the ones who are *already*
crying in his office.
I don't know if crying is *all* they do, but since he's the kind of doctor that
helps people with their problems, I imagine that's most of what they do
because I don't know why anyone would pay a doctor to listen to all the
reasons they're happy. It doesn't make sense.
There's a break in the forest noise.
"Just stand still."
Chuck's voice.
"I just wanna go to sleep."
Corey's voice.
There's a weird bounce in Corey's voice that makes it sound like he's
really scared but too weak to be really scared. Or like his mouth gave up
on talking or something.

I can feel my heart under my jaw.

I don't know what's happening but I know that sound.

It's the same one I heard in my head behind the cabin with Randy. I want to crawl out of my sleeping bag and go over to the fire and pull out the biggest sharpest piece of wood and sneak up behind Chuck and Randy and bring it straight down onto their skulls like Thor would do. Blood and bone and teeth flying everywhere, Corey free and running, all of us free and running, back home, back to somewhere safe. Away from all these beautiful things that are just a lie.

But I do nothing.

My brain is on fire but my body is frozen.

Arms, legs, fingers, toes. Stuck and useless and too scared to do anything about Corey's cries coming from deep in the forest.

His voice sounds so tired.

My mom sounds tired like that but she's way more years older than us. Seven isn't enough years to be that tired.

"Don't cry, you fuckin' baby."

Randy's voice.

Get up, Glenn. Get up, get up, get up.

I want to save my new friend but I am paralyzed. I feel like the trees behind our cabin.

"*Please* stop."

The lions are laughing.

I fail every time Corey calls for help and I don't save him.

I start to count how many times I fail.

"Please stop."

I do nothing.

One.

"Please stop. Please stop."

Two, three.

He's saying please *like he's supposed to. Why aren't they stopping?*

The numbers get higher and Corey's voice gets weaker.

I can't make out Randy's words but they sound wet and fat.

They sound the way he sounds when he's yelling with a cigarette on his lips.

Seven … eight … nine.

My eyes are wet and the stars are starting to bleed.

Everything is black.

downtown city sidewalk

Everything is black. *Where's my phone?* I'm flat against the concrete and
my head is wet and sounds are getting sharper. *Dad?* A blur of fluorescent
light and faces. Faces I don't know, faces I've never seen before. They
are helping me stand and they are asking me if I am okay and I am
saying yes even though I don't know if I am okay. I'm disconnected from
the flurry but oddly relieved that I'm seeing and hearing and smelling
anything at all. Apparently I knocked over some trays of oranges on my
way down. The strangers are picking them up and putting them back in
their boxes. An older Asian man hands me my phone and helps brush the
sidewalk muck off the back of my jacket and I thank him and I love him
and I thank the faces and I love the faces and I start walking and I don't
know how much time has passed and I don't remember exactly what was
happening when I blacked out.
I walk.
I'm not sure where I'm going or why, but I walk.
My phone vibrates in my hand.
"Hello?"
"Stuie? What the hell happened?"
Dad?
"Dad! No idea. I think I fainted."
"Jesus …"
It sounds like he's choking back tears.
"… are you okay?"
I rub my hand on the back of my head and I see that the liquid is clear.
"I guess so. Scared the shit out of me though. I didn't see it coming."

92

There's panic and anger in his voice.

"Go back to the goddamn hospital and have them check you out to make sure you're alright."

"Okay. I'm a block away."

"And call Jay to let him know."

"I'll call him from the hospital."

I stop and I lean against the building and I shield my bald head from the rain and I tell my dad I will call him later to let him know everything is okay. When I stumble through the double doors and back into the infusion room, Elizabeth's eyes go wide in a way that makes me suddenly panic about how I look. She slips her arm under mine and she helps me to the closest chair, even though I'm mostly steady now. Her voice wavers when she asks me what happened.

"I think I just fainted. I don't think it's a big deal."

She takes my blood pressure, runs a penlight past my eyes, tells me to relax. A jolt of heat shoots through me, images of waking up on the sidewalk, redblackred pain redblackred, my body a blanket of chicken skin. This all feels so fucking surreal.

Elizabeth registers the shift in my energy and heads to her desk to call Jay. I can tell by the speed and succinctness of her answers that his diagnostic brain is going a mile a minute.

I raise my voice in an attempt to rescue her.

"Just tell Jay to call me. He'll drive you insane."

She smiles, gives him a few *uh-huhs*, tells him I want to talk to him and hangs up like she's just listened to someone speed-read a medical journal. She speaks.

"He's gonna call—"

My phone rings.

"G. What happened?"

"Just a bunch of lightning shit and then I blacked out."

Silence. Too much silence.

"Okay listen, Glenn. Take a cab home after the nurse says you're okay to leave. None of this walking home stuff."

"I don't have the money for a cab. I'll just take the sub—"

"—I'll pay you back. Just take a fucking cab."

I have less than two hundred dollars in my bank account on any given day and cabs are never an option.

"I'm not gonna take your money."

"Glenn. Shut up. This isn't about money."

"Says the rich doctor."

He hangs up and I don't blame him.

I'm too close to everything to dream a future for myself and I'm too far away to see it all as anything other than a dream. I take a cab home knowing I'll never ask him for the money.

my apartment, forty minutes later

I open the door and I can barely see Jen through the steam billowing up from the stove. Danny is straddling her hip, tucked under one arm as she stirs a pan of ground beef with the other. She tastes a small spoonful and the sight—the pure ordinariness of it—makes my chest suddenly feel heavy and taut. A lead dental X-ray apron draped over my lungs.
I pre-miss simple little moments like this. I've felt glimpses of this over the past couple weeks, but it feels heavier each time. It's a strange kind of mourning for something very much alive.
She fans her mouth to cool her test bite as she speaks.
"How'd it go?"
The smell overwhelms and nauseates me.
"Went fine until I left."
She turns, purses her brow.
My heart sinks. I want to reach out and hold her face in my hand.
I want to hold her, hold Danny as he holds her, hold them both, consume them both.
"What happened?!"
"I fainted. I think."
"You *think?*"
Danny catches my eye and his smile swallows the room.
"I mean I *did* faint. It wasn't a big deal, though."
She turns off the stove and passes Danny over to me and I lean in to kiss her and she flinches.
I'm a stranger.

I hold a two-second funeral in my head before I shift my affection to Danny's head, inhaling the worriless scent of his skin.

I kiss him until his hair is almost damp.

"Really, Glenn? It wasn't a big deal?"

She's annoyed that I continue to downplay everything and I don't care that she is. Or at least I try to convince myself that I don't care.

I care.

I don't know why I can't just fucking say that to her, but I hope I figure it out soon because I'm starting to see fault lines in her face. The kind of invisible lines that start in her heart and branch out across the rest of her like a spider-cracked windshield. She's scared and I know she wants to scream and I know she wants to peel the pain from my body like a giant layer of dead skin and toss it down the garbage chute, relishing in the sight of it flash-frying in the incinerator.

I stand in the doorway between the kitchen and the dining room and watch her divide everything onto the only two dinner plates we own. Her arms move stiffly and deliberately to the rhythm of her clenching jaw as I speak.

"Jen. Just talk to me."

"About what? I'm fine."

She drops the saucepan into the sink and cranks the hot water faucet to full blast.

"You're not fine."

"I am, Glenn. Go sit. I'll bring the food out in a sec."

"I see the Middle East."

Whenever she's upset, her face sprouts a bunch of scattered red blotches that I jokingly say resembles a map of the Middle East.

She used to laugh when I'd point it out.

It used to be enough to soften tension between us. It's no longer enough.

"Go sit."

"Okay maybe just Lebanon, Syria and parts of Egypt?"

She slides a wooden spoon into the steaming sink, looks into my eyes, smiles.

She's in there.

Her smile disappears.

Annnnd now she's not.

I walk to the kitchen table, sit, position Danny on my crossed leg, try to make him laugh with the little cartoon noises I make with my mouth. He doesn't laugh. It's almost like I've forgotten that he only laughs at things resembling pain.

"Oh, right. Funny isn't your thing, Tiny Hitler."

I contort my face to make it look like someone just plunged a knife in my belly. He laughs hard.

Jen sets the plates down and pulls herself in as I speak.

"I'm telling you, I think this kid might be a Nazi."

She gives me a courtesy smile, picks up her fork, exhales, sets it back down, speaks.

"I know you don't think I'm worried about you—"

"—I *never* said that, Jen."

"Let me finish."

I make the zipper gesture across my lips.

Her eyes turn to glass and she swallows a couple times in silence as Danny pinches the skin of my chest.

"Glenn. Listen. I'm scared. I'm really scared. If I cry every time I get scared, I'll never stop crying. And I know crying is exactly what this thing wants …"

She looks up at the ceiling as if she's including a ghost in the conversation.

"… And I won't give it the satisfaction."

I love that she feels this way. I love that her words make me feel like I'm not alone, that we'll attack everything together, that we won't give it the satisfaction of our tears.

All of it. The cracks, the desperation, the missing time, the secrets, the fear, the weakness, the shame. My heart feels almost fully calm for the first time in months. She knew I needed to hear those words and I love that she had the courage to say them.

I love all of it.

I love all of it—even if she never said any of it, not a word.

All those words were daydreams.

Instead, we're just siting here in silence, moving uneaten food around our plates. I feel like I did the other night when I was with the girl who looked like a stoplight because I don't know what's real and what's just what I wish were real.

It wasn't real.

Jen hasn't said a word since she sat down.

Fuck.

I take a sip of ginger ale and I watch her eat, the steam from her plate occasionally softens my view of her eyes as she stares at the couch behind me. The ice twinkles in my glass. The forks continue to scrape.

She never said any of it.

I've never wanted to hear Danny scream more in my life.

"I love you."

Her first words startle me.

Oh my God. Real words.

She spoke three real words that said the same thing as all of the imaginary ones in my daydream. I look into her eyes and I start to cry. My tears instantly trigger hers and I open my mouth to repeat her words but nothing comes.

I love you, Jen.

She takes a deep breath, scoots her chair next to mine and rests her head on my shoulder. Her head has never felt this heavy before and I'm not sure if it's because my body is weaker or if she's decided to release some of the weight of all this. I hope it's the latter but I worry it may be the start of a kind of wreckage neither of us can see yet. There's a hollowness inside me now that I can't fully make sense of.

I kiss her head and I kiss Danny's head and I try to understand, even for a second, how the hell emptiness can feel this heavy.

train back to boston, the next day

I am coated in a thin cool sweat and my skin is the color of the snow clouds chasing the tracks. I don't need a mirror to know this. I can feel it in the way my blood has stilled. This is how everything is now, standing on the edge of a stomach revolt at every second. That unmistakable roiling in my belly will take a few minutes to pass so I take out my phone.
"Stuie?"
The weakness of his voice chills my blood.
"Hey Pop. You okay? You sound tired."
I hear a faint smile.
"Really? I just finished a 10k Fun Run."
"Okay, asshole. I'm less worried now."
"Hold on for a sec, Stu."
The world speeds by my window as I wait. I think about all the people who live in these houses and apartments and I wonder if they're watching all of this like I am, like the last stretch of film threading through an old projector.
Two-hundred seventy-eight seconds.
"Stuie?"
"That took a while, Dad. Still sitting down to pee?"
"Yeah. I'm still sitting down to pee."
I smile.
"Okay okay. You don't need to get nasty with me. I'm just trying to *understand* you."
He laughs, coughs, inhales sharply, moans.

"You okay Pop?"

"It hurts when I laugh, but it's the only thing that makes me feel good, so screw it."

I feel my belly start to stir again.

"One sec, dad."

I stand, stagger through the aisle of the moving train, push aside the heavy bathroom door, lock myself in, crumple myself onto the floor.

I don't care about the urine stench or the stray pubic hairs or the wad of toilet paper that somehow missed its target. I just want to be ready when the time comes.

"You there, Stuie?"

"Yeah. Sorry. I just locked myself in the bathroom in case I get some news from the South."

"Okay well let's talk about something else then. You're less guarded on the phone."

Is that true?

I stare at the graffiti etched into the steel walls as I try to think of something light to talk about.

"Uhh ... I could read some of the weird stuff people have written on these walls?"

"C'mon, Stuie. Your whole life is a museum of weirdness. How about I just call out a year and you tell me something you remember from it."

"Fine, that works, but before you start, let's just enjoy one of these nuggets of wisdom. This one says ..."

I squint.

"Anthony fucked a bagel.'"

He ignores me.

"How about 1994?"

"Hmm. Let me think."

I don't have to think.

A memory from that year is still so vivid that I feel like I'm reliving it in real time:

It's summer, I have no AC, I'm sweating and annoyed, and I've just spent almost two hours on the phone trying to schedule an appointment. There's no way I'm giving up, though.

It's Saturday in Manhattan. I'll find something.

"No? Okay thanks."

They think I'm fucking crazy.

I hang up the phone and I drag my finger down the page and I call the next hair salon listed in the Yellow Pages. The phone rings several times, way too many times, and I stay on the line because I am determined, and I know I can't be the only one asking this question.

A woman with a thick Spanish accent answers and I speak and she goes quiet and then I go quiet and then she says she doesn't understand what I'm asking, so I repeat myself.

"I'm just wondering if you do hair extensions for men?"

She clicks her tongue and hangs up the phone.

> "Wait. You were trying to get hair extensions? You're joking, right?"
> I feel myself blush.
> "Not joking, Pop."
> He lets out a disappointed sigh.
> "Jesus. Okay, keep going ... I think."

I drag my finger down the page to the next number, call, ask the same question and get a different version of the same response. I'm starting to lose patience. *Why is this so hard?* I was born with a *Jew-fro* and my hair is thick and dark and no matter how hard I try to grow it long, I can't get the Eddie Vedder effect I want: long and wavy and loose. Hair I can hide behind. Hair that matches the image of the misanthrope I believe I've been since I was a kid. The problem is that my hair grows wide, not long. I know they do hair extensions for women all the time and I watch enough movies to know they do it for men all the time too and I'm starting to get really annoyed that the request has been met with so much confusion and disdain.

Five rings and the woman on the other end of the line sounds confused but says exactly what I want to hear.

"Sure! We can do that, yeah."

Oh my God.

My heart starts pounding. I ask her about her schedule and she tells me *come in now.*

Now?

Now!

My hands shake as I write down the address. I'm excited because I've never been to Washington Heights. I shower, get dressed, hop on the express train, my heart is exploding with joy. Jen left for work this morning with me looking like Bob Saget and she will come home to me looking like Chris Cornell. She's going to be so excited.

I get off the subway and the air is thick with cigarettes and fried plantains and bad perfume and I'm pretty sure I'm the only non-Dominican within a hundred miles. I walk the gum-littered catwalk, scan the doorways for building numbers, spot the number I'm looking for. I step back toward the curb and shield my eyes from the sun as I try to get a better look at the building.

I don't see a *Rosa's Hair Salon* sign anywhere.

"Wait. No red flags were going off at this point?"
"Not really, Pop. I don't see why there would've been."
"The fact that you *still don't* says everything I need to know."

I walk to the steel panel beside the door, spot a small white handwritten tag labeled *ROSA*, press the button next to it. The door lets out a loud buzz and I grab the handle and I walk over to the base of a steep set of stairs and I see the paint is peeling off the handrail in long strips like an old psoriatic arm.

A woman yells *hello* from several floors up and I climb until I am breathless and face-to-face with a short, pear-shaped middle-aged woman I assume is Rosa.

"Rosa?"

"Clem?"

"Sure."

I extend my hand and I tell her it's nice to meet her and she smiles and escorts me into a room bustling with several Black and Latin women. Half customers, half hairdressers. She points to a chair in the corner of the room, tells me to take my jacket off, tells me *go and get comfortable.* The din in the room suddenly goes from henhouse to library as I feel a long, unrelenting wave of regret wash over me and settle in. I sit down and I try my best to exude an air of nonchalance as I flip through a copy of *Ebony* magazine, furrowing my brow occasionally as if I've stumbled upon an article that might just be helpful for an idiot like me.

"Okay Clem. What did you want to do today?"

I feel myself start to blush. Everyone in the room is waiting for me to speak like they're waiting for me to announce the new Pope. I try to speak softly but my nerves are forcing me to project more than I'd like.

"I want to grow my hair long but it's too thick so I was thinking that if

I added extensions, it would weigh my hair down long enough until it grows out on its own."

A stifled laugh ripples across the room as I continue. I'm too embarrassed to look up.

"So I wanted to do something like Eddie Vedder. Like shoulder length or something. Like the way he had it in Pearl Jam's *Unplugged* session."

She smiles politely and runs her fingers through my 70s-era Travolta feather wave. Then, a bigger smile. She looks at me in the mirror and nods as if she knows *exactly* what I have in mind.

I feel like a suicide bomber standing in the middle of a café wearing a vest that didn't detonate.

She walks to a padlocked closet, takes out a handful of long, clear packages, spreads them out across my lap and I point to one, say *I like this color* and she says *they're all the same* in a way that tells me my only job right now is to just sit and wait until this is all over.

> "What the hell, Stuie?"
> "What?"
> "Why didn't you just leave?!"
> "I didn't want to hurt her feelings. What was I supposed to say anyway? *Sorry Rosa, these aren't the hair extensions I had in mind?!*"
> "Yes! Or how about just telling her the truth?"
> "I don't know."
>   I *do* know. I was protecting her from the truth the same way I've protected him from the truth. As if they're one and the same.
> "Should I continue, Pop?"
> "Obviously! I love a good car accident."

The henhouse din returns quickly once the women in the room realize I'm not insane, just pathetic.

The process takes longer than I could've possibly imagined and I do my best to make small talk. She tells me about her husband and her kids and her family back home in the Dominican Republic and she asks about mine but she doesn't listen to the answers. I ask her how often she does men's hair and she tells me *all the time* in a way that confirms *never*. I try not to look into the mirror because I imagine the worst and don't want to think about how much I will have to pay for this huge lapse in judgment.

I think about all the red flags I ignored along the way as I take my fourth full pass of the same issue of *Ebony*.

Idiot. Every place you called hung up for a reason.

Several hours pass.

Rosa places her hands on my shoulders the way a massage therapist does when they're signaling the end of the session.

"All done, Clem. Whatcha think?"

When I look up into the mirror, I force my eyes to focus on the wall behind me so I don't have to actually look at whatever the hell is now stuck to my head.

"Looks perfect. Thanks, Rosa!"

I stand, pay her, give her a hefty tip and slip my coat back on. I give her a hearty *"I'll see you soon!"* as I walk out the door. I don't make it three full steps before the place erupts in a mix of howls and laughter that I've genuinely never heard outside a sitcom laugh track.

"Stuie."

"Dad. I know what you're gonna say."

Silence.

I guess I don't.

As I walk toward the subway, I catch my reflection in a storefront window.

Rick James.

I fucking look like Rick James.

Yes, my hair is long now. But it's also still wide.

Very wide.

I spot an old school barbershop two doors down from the entrance to the subway and I walk in and find myself staring into a male version of the same sudden and stunned silence that greeted me at Rosa's.

I'm sweating and red and I ask the barber closest to the door how long I'll have to wait for a haircut.

He says *it depends*.

I tell him I want to shave it all off.

He smiles like he's proud of me for coming to my senses and he tells me I'm next.

Twenty minutes later I walk to the subway looking like a rejected extra who accidentally wandered off the set of *Romper Stomper*.

Silence.

Silence.

I can hear my father breathing.

Silence. Breathing.

"Dad?"

Click.

Dial tone.

I call him back and he doesn't pick up.

I laugh because I know this is his punch line and I know he is sitting in bed and he is laughing and he is not thinking about dying and I am not thinking about dying and right now that is enough.

train platform, three hours later

My father is on the platform waiting for me, bundled up and wincing
from the hard rush of wind I dragged here from New York. His skin is
the color of old concrete and his cheekbones are sharper and his eyes are
deeper set. His belly has swapped out its subtler parenthesis shape for a
tighter symmetrical one.
I'm surprised he's out of bed and even more surprised to see him here
against every wish of his body.
I am proud of him and I am worried about him.
The doors open and I wait until the hemorrhage of people slows to a
trickle. He nervously scans the crowd and there's something about his
eyes that tell me his worry is more than just making sure this is the right
train. I think we both look for each other now in a way that has nothing
to do with location. It's the searching of drowning.
I thread myself between two straggling commuters and I wrap my arms
around him and I hold him like we are waiting to be buckled in and
airlifted from a rooftop after a hurricane.
He doesn't want to let go.
I don't want to let go.

my father's kitchen, twenty minutes later

We drop my bag off at the house and Andrea slips into the kitchen
to hug me hello, the flowery citrus smell of her perfume quieting my
jackhammer heart.
She turns, runs her fingers through my father's hair as Julia skips through
the room with her little pink stereo blasting some song about Barbie
going to some kind of party. I shake my head, tell them I don't know
how they do it, tell them the lead singer's voice sounds like an abortion
set to synth music.
Andrea clicks her tongue and shakes her head at my choice of analogy.
"Well, bad music aside, *this* looks like a happier Papa. Someone who's glad
to have his son back."
My father holds back a smile because he doesn't want to give either of us
the satisfaction of being right about what brings him joy.
He claps his gloved hands together, speaks.
"Feel like taking a walk to the coffee shop, Stu?"
"I'm not really up for a walk but I'd love it if you brought me back
something. Maybe a decaf latte and ... I don't know, surprise me."
Andrea laughs.
Oh shit.
She gives me an don't-forget-he-doesn't-like-to-be-laughed-at look.
I did forget. *Good pitcher, bad catcher.*
She pulls her hair back into a makeshift bun and she whispers "I'll leave
you boys to it," as she slips out of the room.
I tighten my scarf, adjust his parka collar, slip my arm around the top of

his back and ease him down the front steps.

He shrugs me off.

"Enough with the kid gloves."

"But that's *literally* what they are, Pop"

No laugh, no smile, no anything. His silence is highlighted by the silence of the snow that covers every inch of the neighborhood. The whole tableau looks like a painting you'd see in a motel room, a kind of small-town uniformity that makes it feel like it's been staged for tour buses.

We make our way down the block to the coffee shop, get our drinks, take the table next to the door. The floor-to-ceiling window is steamed over from the older couple getting up to leave. I love how the steam erases the world outside, how it leaves us with both daylight and privacy. Every other seat in the place is taken but there's a quiet electricity in the air as if these people are all paid extras in our shitty movie scene.

He speaks for the first time since we left the house.

"We have to talk, Stuie."

"Oh Jesus. Nothing good ever comes after *we have to talk*."

"I wanna have a plan for after I die ..."

My throat tightens as I try to shut down the wave of emotion barreling through me. I can see he's getting dragged out to sea and I want to be the rock he can hold onto. I take a deep breath, wipe away a rogue tear with the back of my glove, pretend it's just a cold-weather straggler.

"... Like your sister. I know she's only eleven, but I think this'll be harder on her than she'll probably show and I want you and your brother to be a part of her life. She's so smart and interested in life in a way neither of you guys were and I don't want that to get snuffed out by the day-to-day shit."

I start to speak and he raises his hand to stop me. His eyes well up, his breathing gets shallow, he bites his lip to stop any of it from unraveling. I speak anyway.

"You love Julia more than *me!* How's that possible? Did you hear that music? *'Come on Barbie, let's go potty?'*"

He ignores my stupid attempt to erase the mess and I don't blame him.

"—I wrote her a stack of birthday cards. They're in the top right-hand drawer of my desk."

I want him to stop speaking. I don't want the stain of his words to set.

"Dad—"

"Let me finish."

"G'head."

"They all have dates on them. Andrea's gonna handle it all but just in case something happens, please make sure you give her one every year."

I'm going to be dead soon too, Pop.

"And tell her I love her and I'm sorry I couldn't—"

"—Dad."

His shoulders slump deeper with each new directive as if he's mapping his path to the casket.

"Stuie, please."

"Dad, shut up for a second. I promise I'll do whatever it is you want or need me to do but I really believe when you put this shit out there, you give it shape. If you *say* you're dying, then you're dying. *I'm* not dying and *you're* not dying, okay?"

There's a hollowness in his eyes, the same dull gray kind of resignation I've seen in the eyes of the horses that pull the carriages in Central Park.

Silence.

His eyes dilate.

"Stuie…"

Silence.

"… I'm scared."

A tear slips from his eye, follows the crease of his nose, disappears into the crack of his lips. I grab his head and pull it against my shoulder. There are no more bones in my heart left to break.

I point to my watch and tell him he has twenty minutes to discuss morbid practicalities, but we'll need to move on after that.

"Okay, Pop. Clock starts now. Besides the birthday cards for Julia, what else?"

"I have a couple things in the vault that I want you guys to have, but the paperwork's with Andrea. She'll take care of all of it."

"What's in the vault?"

"Family stuff. Jewelry, that kinda thing. I just want you guys to split it up and hold onto a few things for Julia for when she's older."

"Just promise me it's not gonna be like grandma's vault."

He tilts his head like a dog hearing the word *treat*.

"Really, Dad? You already forgot?"

When my grandmother was dying, she kept telling my father and uncle that there was something in her bank vault that she didn't want either of them to see until after she died.

"Promise me, guys. Do not open it until I'm gone."

She was vehement every time she mentioned it, and she mentioned
it often.

"Do NOT open it until I'm gone."

They were both tortured by their own different theories:

Were they adopted?

Did my grandfather fake his own death?

Was there a large pile of money waiting to be divvied up?

When she died a few weeks later, my father and uncle made a beeline
for the bank vault to find that the only thing in the giant steel box was
a small note written on a folded piece of lined paper that read:

> "In the event of my death or the death of my wife,
> Tony gets the vacuum cleaner."

My dad and I laugh as the sun dips below the trees outside the
coffee shop.

"Who the hell was Tony anyway, Pop?"

"Their next-door neighbor. That guy with the bad toupee."

"Did you guys actually give him the vacuum cleaner?"

"He'd already taken it. He took almost everything, actually. Her TV, her
dining room set, a bunch of other crap."

We bundle up and walk back out the front door as a dampened ding of a
bell announces our exit.

Tony gets the vacuum cleaner.

I'm still laughing.

The street back to my father's house is pristine again. The new snow has
erased our old footprints and the streetlamps have painted a path of large
yellow circles showing us the way back home. I want to speak as we walk,
but my mouth is frozen shut. I want to tell him everything. Everything
I've never told him. I want to tell him because I know he's the only one
who'll be able to piece together the right words, the right thoughts, the
right roads for the right map that will pull me from this secret place. But
I also know deep inside my pathetic duct-taped heart, this secret is a mess
I can't ask him to help me clean up.

That window has closed.

Cancer is maximum capacity.

Cancer is a weight that can't be stacked.

We walk and we walk and we walk and a feeling of dread passes through
me like the shadow of a passing airplane.

day 10

I wake up inside a dream that's nothing like a dream.
Last night doesn't feel real even though I can tell it *was* by the way
Corey's staring at the dirt.
Everything feels louder now, even colors and smells.
The crackle of bacon. The poofs of black smoke as Randy pours someone's
full canteen over the coals. The sun on my neck that isn't warm. My pee-
soaked sleeping bag that I punched into its shiny new red sack.
It all feels the way barf smells.
We line up and set off on our four-hour hike back to camp, a four-hour
blur of sound and smell and light.
Just melting snow and moss and mud and pine needles and secrets.
Fuck. You.
I know I'm not supposed to even think these bad words but they fit what
I feel right now as Chuck leads us back to the dirt road that runs through
the middle of camp.
He kicks our cabin door open and a cloud of dust flies off his pant leg
and falls to the porch like glitter.
It's the first beautiful thing the sun has made today.
I feel safer with this sun than I did with the one we left behind on top of
that mountain.
Everything feels slower and I don't know if that is a good thing or a bad
thing. Time just feels different.
I hope this feeling goes away.
"Alright, ladies. Shower time. Put your shit on your bunks and grab your
towels and soap. And no bathing suits. We're not babies anymore."

I don't know why Chuck is still here or why he's giving us orders but I start counting.

Fourteen boys.

Two counselors.

One long shower stall.

Eight showerheads.

If I go with the first group of guys, it'll be six boys plus Randy and Chuck.

Total of eight showerheads and eight bodies.

If I go with the second group, it'll be eight boys and no counselors.

Same number of showerheads, zero counselors.

It's an easy choice.

I take my time gathering my bathroom stuff.

Randy and Chuck are the first in flip-flops and towel skirts and the first out the door.

Thank God.

I turn around to see who the other lucky ones are:

Corey, Mark, David, Mike, Matt, Josh, Owen.

I make eye contact with Mark and I see the corners of his mouth turn up in a weird smile.

He knows.

Corey's eyes haven't left the ground since this morning. I think they broke him open last night in a way he can never be fixed.

I walk over and I talk to his scalp.

"You okay?"

Stupid question.

He shrugs. I don't know how to make this feel normal.

I make a joke because it always makes things feel normal in my house when my dad yells at my mom.

"Wanna take a shit in Randy's hat?"

His scalp wrinkles above his ears.

A smile?

I've never used bad words and I hardly even think them in my head but now they're the only words I can think of.

It's like they have sharper teeth than the words I already know.

I open Corey's trunk and I grab his towel and the shiny green bag with his bathroom stuff in it and I push them against his chest.

Thunderclap.

"Mark! David! Get your shit and hustle out to the showers. Two open showers. Hustle!"

Why's Randy still here?

I feel my heart trying to kick itself out through my throat.

Shit. Shitshitshit.

"Josh, Owen, Corey, Glenn, Matt, Mike. You ladies hang back. You'll go with us."

Chuck stands in the doorway and leans against the door.

Even though the sun is behind him, I can see something wrong with his face, his cheeks are puffy and his pimple scars are shaded like tiny half-moons. He tries to make things sound normal.

"Did you guys have fun on the overnight?"

Silence.

Randy lets out the wrong kind of laugh.

"Aw. Those don't look like happy faces. Let's go around the cabin and each of you tell us your favorite part of the hiking trip. Owen? Why don't you start—"

"Bacon!"

We all laugh the right kind of laugh.

Silence.

"Glenn?"

"Bacon!"

Another laugh.

Something inside me told me this would be a funny answer even though I'm not sure why. I just know that whatever I said changed the way Randy was standing. Like it was enough to get him to take the noose off my neck.

"Corey?"

Silence.

"Corey. Look at me."

Corey lifts his head and looks over at Chuck.

Fuck.

"Hey! I said look at *me*."

The squishing sound of wet flip flops breaks the silence as Jeremy runs up the stairs on his way back from the showers and pushes past Chuck and onto his bunk.

He senses none of the tension in the room and he starts to tell us all how John makes the funniest armpit farts in the shower, how the water makes them so much juicier, how Prell makes them louder, how they all laughed until John let out a real fart from laughing so hard.

The room stays silent as Corey continues to stare down the shape in the doorway.

Jeremy shrugs and grabs his Mad Magazine and rolls onto his belly and starts to flip through it like he's at home in his own bed.

I wish I was Jeremy.

All this air in the cabin still invisible and clean.

The rest of the guys from the first group run into the cabin and start snapping towels, laughing the right kind of laughs, messing around with different gadgets from home.

Randy uses the sudden commotion to herd the rest of us out to the showers. The happy chirp chirp of Adam's electronic football game feels like it's laughing at us as we leave.

I count how many steps it takes to get there.

Ninety-six.

We line up under the showers and we turn on our faucets and the hot water is pretty much gone.

We all stand there naked and shivering and silent.

Six boys, two counselors. Eight total.

Randy shampoos his curly mop at one end of the room and Chuck rubs a bar of green soap against his privates like he's trying to use it all up.

It feels like he wants us all to look but none of us do.

Corey stares at the drain in front of him as it overflows with a mountain of graybrown bubbles. The bubbles look like snow that a million cars have already driven on.

Josh turns his shower off, grabs his towel, steps into his flip-flops and disappears.

Seven.

Another faucet squeak.

Six.

I let the water pound my chest as I watch a small cloud of moths circle the only light bulb in the room.

I don't remember who told me this, but I guess moths make their way around the sky using the light of the moon and wind up lost and trapped like these ones when they mistake light bulbs for the moon.

It's sad.

They're just trying to live a regular life but they wind up tired and dead on some bathroom floor nowhere near home.

"Hey! Don't use the *whole* bar of soap!"

Owen laughs as he speaks, pointing at Chuck's crotch.

"You're gonna use up all the soap!"

Shit.

Silence.

Shit. Shut up, Owen.

Runrunrunrun, Glenn. Run.

I crank my faucet off, grab Corey's arm and we lock eyes.

He understands what my eyes are telling him.

He understands it in a way neither of us could've ever understood it a few days ago.

I see sky and trees through the gap between the top of the door and the frame and I walkrun over to our towels and grab what I can without looking. Corey is glued to my side and doing everything exactly like I am. I kick open the door with my foot and we squint from the sun and we take off running. Running and half-blind and barefoot and naked and counting a number of footsteps I can't remember anymore.

The other guys laugh as we burst into the cabin.

I bet we look crazy.

We never fake a laugh or pretend we're being funny. We just get dressed and climb onto our bunks and stare at the open door.

My heart is behind my ears while I count the missing ones.

Four.

Two minutes pass.

Wet footsteps up the porch stairs.

It's Evan and he's drying his hair with a towel as he walks through the door.

Three.

My heart sinks.

Three.

Two lions, one lamb.

Ten minutes pass.

Another ten.

Owen walks through the door like his bones are made out of balsa wood. His head is down and the light in his eyes, the light that yelled *bacon* without thinking, the light that tried to save Chuck from accidentally using up all his soap, is gone.

Owen is a moth now. A moth tricked by a light pretending to be a moon.

my father's living room, next morning

I can smell the sweetness of Andrea's breath as she shakes my shoulder.
"Glenn. Sorry, sorry. Your dad's appointment's in a couple hours and
I know you said you wanted to shower first."
I cover my mouth to spare her my morning breath.
She smiles, tells me she's used to bad smells by now, tells me she'll let
me wake Dad up when I'm ready. I collect the blankets off the living
room couch, fold them, set them on the floor in the corner. They're
starting to smell from too many nights of chemo sweat. The worst
kind of sweat. A purging sweat that might actually be purging nothing.
A snake shedding its skin with no sign of the new skin underneath.
I walk to the bathroom, sit down, pee, stand back up.
Fuck. No no no.
The bowl is ruby red. My stomach drops to my feet. It's the same panic
I've felt so many times before.
Fuckfuckfuck.
I start to sweat and my mind races with every possibility it can imagine,
always starting with the Horrific and Improbable and never quite
making it down the line to the Likely. My stomach is bleeding my
kidneys are bleeding my liver is collapsing my bones are splintering
everything inside my chest is melting and plunging through me like a
burst sewage line and there is no way to stop it or slow it and I am not
with Danny and I am not with Jen and I need to grab my father and
hoist him over my shoulder and carry him through the snow along the
train tracks until I get home, until I can die with the people I love all
in one place all in one bed.

I open my phone and I call Jay.

"G? Everything okay?"

A drop of sweat slides off my chin, hits the toilet water, scrambles the reflection of my face.

"I just peed blood."

"Was it bright red as it was coming out of you?"

"I don't know."

"How do you not *know*?"

"I was sitting down."

"To pee?"

Fear turns my legs to gelatin and I lean over and vomit into the bowl. It comes fast and strong and the residue it leaves on my tongue is thick, synthetic and sticky like the smell of a black garbage bag left in a hot car. I start hyperventilating. *Breathebreathebreathe.* I put my palms on either side of the sink, breathe in, breathe out, breathe in, breathe out, turn, pull myself onto the counter, lean back against the mirror, start counting the dead bugs in the light fixture.

I lift the phone back up to my ear.

"G? You okay?"

I spit, wipe my mouth with my sleeve.

"I'm here, I'm fine …"

My breathing gets shallow.

"… I'm fucking scared, JJ—"

"Glenn. Breathe. You're not gonna die. There are a hundred fairly benign reasons for a little blood in the urine and given your treatment, it's not that unusual. Just breathe."

I exhale, my breath stutters to the rhythm of my pulse.

"Okay, JJ. I'm breathing."

"Are you driving your dad to the hospital today?"

"I'm supposed to, yeah."

"Okay good. Call me when you get there and I'll arrange for you to get things checked out."

I thank him, take off my clothes, get in the shower, breathe in breathe out breathe in breathe out as the hot water pelts my neck. I pee again and the rose tint is barely visible now. It quiets my heart.

I towel off, get dressed, trudge upstairs, set my hand on my dad's bedroom door like I'm feeling it for the presence of a fire on the other side.

The door makes a hiss against the carpet as I push it open.

A slow unveiling of my father's legs and feet. They're pale, puffy and dimpled. Inflatable pool toys left out in the sun too long.

He clears his throat, sighs, "Come in, Stuie."

I push the door all the way open and I tiptoe in as if he's still sleeping.

"Sorry, Dad. I didn't know how to wake you up without startling you."

"Great job. The sound of the village idiot mouth-breathing behind my door wasn't creepy at all."

"Okay, asshole. Well, the *village idiot* has to get you to your appointment."

I don't tell him about what happened downstairs or the tests I have to get done when we get to the hospital. He swings his legs off the side of the bed, clears his throat.

"I don't even know why I have to go to these appointments anymore. It's not like he's gonna tell me the cancer is all gone and I should go run a marathon or something."

"You don't know that, Dad."

He knows it. I know it. We both know it.

We make our way downstairs, through the kitchen, out the front door and stop only to grab his puke bowl and small green hand towel. He rarely makes it a full hour without vomiting now. Outside, he grabs the handrail with both hands as he makes his way down each icy step. This sight crushes me, another gash in my windshield.

I ease him into the passenger seat, skate around the back of the car, flop down behind the wheel and slam the door shut.

We sit and we watch our breaths tumble into the dashboard as we wait for the car to heat up.

"You know what I'm gonna do, Stuie?"

"What?"

"When I die, I'm gonna send you a message from the afterlife so you know I'm okay."

"How you gonna do that?"

"I'll send you a message through the first song you hear when you turn on the radio."

I laugh.

"Okay, Pop. Let's practice. Pretend you're dead."

"What?"

He doesn't like that I'm making light of this.

"Pretend you're dead. I'll turn on the radio."

"I'm being serious, Stuie."

"I know. So let's make sure I'm doing it right. Play dead."

He smirks, tilts his head to side, opens his mouth, hangs his tongue off to the side.

"C'mon, Pop. You're not Terry Schiavo. Pretend like you're *actually* dead."

He closes his mouth and I start to fake cry.

"Oh, Papa. I miss you. Please send me *some* kind of sign to let me know you're here. *Any* sign at all."

I turn on the radio.

Dancing Queen by ABBA.

Silence.

We erupt in laughter.

"Is there something you need to tell me, Dad?!"

He laughs coughs laughs.

"Just drive, Stuie."

I drive and the snow starts to fall. The sky is trying to erase all of this again. I love this moment and I don't want to erase it.

At the end of the street, a tree that has broken under the weight of the snow is lying in the middle of the road. I drive onto the sidewalk because it's the only way through.

hospital parking garage, eighty-one minutes later

As we pull in, the white metal box yells, sticks out its tongue, raises its arm, swallows our car. Everything that was once routine and invisible is now alive and ominous. Everything is a threat, an enemy, a monster. This hospital parking garage is the monster I hate most because I know someday soon it will swallow us both and stop spitting us back out. As it is, every time it does spit us back out, we aren't the same as we were when we came in. We're lesser, weaker, further from ourselves.

"There are parking spots everywhere, Glenn."

"Sorry, Pop."

I haven't been paying attention. I pull into the next available spot.

"That's okay, Stu. We can take a cab from here."

I laugh. We're in the furthest spot from the elevator.

I back out and circle the lot until I find a closer spot.

I pull in, shift the car into neutral, pretend I've forgotten how to brake. He smacks my arm.

"Just park the damn car, Stuie."

I slam the brake pedal, turn off the ignition, stare at him in silence. I'm annoying him, and I love that I am. He feels more alive like this, more like my dad. He opens his door and swings his legs around like he's dismounting a horse. His back is toward me but I can see the pain in the corners of his eyes.

We ride the elevator in silence as it lowers us deeper into the belly of the hospital, the sharp stench of decay hits us like an uppercut to the jaw the moment it finally rejects us.

"Stuie. You okay?"

"Yeah. Just having one of those moments where I wish things felt like they used to …"

I continue as we walk through the main lobby, dodge a speeding gurney, weave past a pack of chattering geriatrics.

"… The parking garage, the elevator, this hospital. Now it all feels like it's part of a long pipeline that empties into some fucking lion's den and I'm just so tired of getting thrown around like this."

He stops in the middle of a stream of scuttling scrubs, turns to look at me.

"Where's all this coming from?"

"I don't know."

I do know.

He motions to a row of chairs against the wall, says *let's go sit for second.*
He's putting his own pain aside for me and I don't like that he is. I want to take care of *him.*

"I could explain all the psychology crap to you, Glenn, but I think you know why everything feels this way. You know exactly why you're pissed."

"It's more than pissed, Dad."

"Stuie. Look at me. You're okay. This all feels scary as hell and it all feels unfair—of *course* it does, but—"

Unfair? You're too late to protect me from unfair.

"—it's not about you and it's not about me and it's not about any of these people here. It just *is.*"

He doesn't skip a beat as an orderly steers an empty wheelchair around us.

"And you've gotta be a narcissistic asshole to think any of this is personal or that we're unique in any way …"

His bottom lip starts to quiver.

"… All we can do is try not to die. That's it. We live, we live as well as we can, then we die. No lion's den, no conspiracies. The elevator *is* just a fucking elevator."

A tear slides down his cheek and hits his gray sweatpants.

A charcoal-colored bullet hole to the thigh.

reception area, ten minutes later

Almost every seat on our sinking ferry is taken today and we have no
other choice but to lean against the wall on either side of a plastic tree as
we wait. I push aside its dusty branches and speak.
"How ya doin' over there?"
He seems to be supporting all his body weight against the wall and I can
tell he's uncomfortable.
Help him out, Glenn.
I look around the room, find the healthiest looking non-patient, walk
over, ask him to give up his seat for my father. He says *no thanks* like I
just asked him if he wanted a second helping of pot roast.
I smell coconut.
Shampoo?
I repeat my request.
He declines again.
Hand lotion?
"What kind of cancer do you have?"
"I don't. I'm just waiting for my friend."
"Perfect. Then do me a quick favor?"
Stop, Glenn.
I turn to watch the snow settle into the trees outside the window but it
does nothing to calm me.
"Get the fuck outta the seat."
Stopstop, Glenn.
His eyes go wide the way any sane person's would.

I'm sorry I'm sorry I'm sorry.

I'm turning into everything I hate.

As he walks away, I motion to my father to come over and take the open seat. He's been watching all of this play out and catches the guy as he walks by and says something to him that I can't hear, but it's something that has the movement of gratitude and remorse. The guy pats my father on the shoulder with an understanding kindness and they walk over together. I shake the man's hand, apologize profusely, tell him I'll buy him something expensive from the gift shop, *maybe even gum.* His face softens and it settles my heart even though I know I don't deserve the arms of his eyes.

exam room, twenty-seven minutes later

Everything is clinical and cold. Every surface painted the whitegray of wet bone. I don't know why I haven't noticed this color palette at any of the previous appointments but it must have something to do with this thing that keeps taking control of my brain. Part of its insidious hold on me is to wipe even the simple things clean of beauty.

I glance at the caged clock on the wall.

"Hey Pop, I have to run downstairs for a bit but I shouldn't be gone long."

"What? Why?"

"I'll explain later but Jay wants me to get a couple quick tests while I'm in the building."

"He can't wait until you get back to New York?"

"He can, but he's neurotic."

Another lie to protect a person I love. Another lie that dumps more kerosene on the flame deep inside me that never goes out.

"Okay, Stuie. Well if I get done before you, I'll just find a seat in the waiting room."

"It should be quick, Dad."

I kiss his forehead, make my way down to the lab, give the intake nurse my name and she smiles and whisks me to a back room like a high-ranking diplomat.

Thank you, Jay.

The room is antiseptic and empty except for a small beige school desk with collapsible wings and a metal rolling cart packed with a dull rainbow of glass vials. I open the wings, squeeze into the seat and I wait.

The clock keeps a rhythm half the speed of my heart. I wait and I wait and I wait. *No cage on this clock.* I wait for what feels like days and my legs bounce uncontrollably like I'm pedaling a machine that's keeping me alive and I'm tired and I'm scared and I'm worried about my dad and I don't want to wait. I don't want to find another reason to be scared, another reason I need to be scared. I just want to run and run and fucking run.

Pine trees.

I don't know where the smell is coming from, but I smell it.

I smell trees.

The clouds outside the window are darkening.

I want to chase the daylight, outrun the sky, stop the march of the shadows that chase me every second of every day.

Run run run run run fucking run.

I stand, open the door, bolt through the lab, out the main entrance and onto the street. I run and I run and I don't know where I'm running to, but the snowflakes are falling like wet doilies and I love that they are because they're big enough to swallow me up, hide me, bury me, bury us.

I stop at an intersection I don't recognize.

I don't know how long I've been running or how far away I am from the hospital, but I know that I'm lost.

I am freezing and I don't remember how I got here.

day 17

I don't remember how I got here.

I am lying on my back again and I'm watching the upside-down trees outside the window go from green to orangegreen.

I want to lie on my belly like I used to but Owen told me and Corey to *protect our bottoms.*

I laughed when he used the word *bottom* but Corey hasn't laughed for a long time and neither has Owen so maybe he's not trying to be funny.

Randy and Chuck are laughing.

They're in their room smoking gross cigarettes and yelling at each other over the radio playing that song *Tequila Sunrise.* I know the song because Nate plays his Eagles records all the time at home and I hate it.

"Shoes on, faggots!"

Randy pokes his head out from behind the bed-sheet curtain and yells to all of us like we're the ones playing the loud music.

Corey and Owen and Mark and I never take our shoes off.

We don't talk about it but I think we're figuring out how to give Randy and Chuck less things to notice.

"Phone home time!"

They told us we would get to call our parents *once* while we're here even though we'd *probably be having too much fun* to want to waste time on the phone.

I want to waste time on the phone.

I want to waste all the time I have.

We hop out of our bunks and line up single-file outside the cabin like we always do before we do something fun that's not fun.

Corey and Owen and Mark and I make sure we don't line up together. This was Corey's idea because he thinks it will be harder to pull us out of line if we're not together.

He never actually told me that but I think that's why.

It's hard to understand anything Corey does anymore because he doesn't say much and everything he does say feels like winter. Pointy and cold. Randy walks out onto the porch, stretches, sees that we're all lined up and quiet. He mumbles through an unlit cigarette.

"Gooh lil soldiers."

He slides his hand down into his running shorts and scratches his balls and it seems like his hand is in there forever, like he won't take it out until all of us see it. I don't get why his penis and balls are so important to him. They're just a pile of skin and hair and they're not big or strong like a leg or an arm.

He walks down the line, running his hand back and forth across his sunburnt chest, watching each of us like we're an army getting ready to attack a castle or something.

I smell the suntan lotion on his skin as he passes and my heart starts trying to kick my ribs.

There's a weird buzzy silence.

The hissing sound of wind through the trees and the sticky click of Randy's flip-flops.

The sound of my heart drowns out both.

"Glenn."

Shit.

His breath is against my ear, warm wet mediciney.

"Look at me …"

I turn my head to face him but I let my eyes focus on the tree over his shoulder so I don't have to be eaten up again like I was behind the cabin. He stares at me as he raises his voice to address all the other guys in line.

"You each get five minutes. Tell your folks how much fun we're having."

He starts to laugh in a way that feels far away, like I'm watching his mouth through the wrong end of a telescope.

"Maybe tell 'em you can't *believe* you only get a few more days here."

A few more days?

I hear Chuck laughing in the distance adding *tell 'em to send whiskey.* Randy tells Chuck to *shut the fuck up, act professional* and then tells us to ignore him.

127

I like when they don't get along because they feel weaker, like their
teeth are softer.
Flip flop flip flop flip flop flip flop flip flop.
Randy gets back to the front of the line, turns, tells us to follow him
to the mess hall and tells us *no talking* even though some of the guys
never listen to him when he says no talking.
The dust from our feet makes a cartoon stink cloud as we walk
through camp.
The kids in the other cabins watch as we pass by and it's almost like
they know something is wrong.
We make our way past the baseball field, around the horse stable, across
the empty archery range and up the squeaky steps to the dining hall.
When we get to the double doors, Randy turns and tells us to sit and wait
at the picnic tables, *wait until I call your name and bring you in.*
He puts his giant paw against my back, shoves me inside, points to the
pale-yellow phone hanging on the back wall, tells me to sit in the chair
below it and wait for him to dial.
I sit and stare at the big rotten tooth with numbers.
I don't know what to say to my mom and dad when they pick up.
The truth would make them feel worse than me finding the eggs last
Easter so I just won't say anything.
I don't know why but thinking this thought slows my heartbeat and
makes me feel safer.
It's like I'm spread across a landmine and my only job is not to move and
I know I can do that.
Randy walks over with a list of typed names and numbers and he tucks
the receiver between his ear and his shoulder and he dials way more
numbers than I've ever seen.
He says *Glenn* through his cigarette, waits, says it again angrier and
louder, waits, hands me the phone, points to the clock on the opposite
wall, says *five minutes* like one of those cops on TV.
"Stuie?"
My father's voice feels warm and cold at the same time.
I want to cry but I know what crying brings so I won't.
"Hi, Dad."
I look up at Randy to make sure I'm doing what I'm supposed to be
doing and his eyelids close in slow motion, like they're saying *good job.*
"You havin' a good time, Stuie?"
No no no no no no no no.

"Yes. I am. I am having a good time."

I hope my dad will hear how stiff my words sound and he'll understand what's happening and he'll tell me to stay on the line while he sends a helicopter to swoop in and rescue me.

He speaks.

"Uh-oh—"

He understood! Thank you thank you thank you God.

"—it sounds like maybe you didn't do what I told you—"

Huh?

"—I specifically said 'whatever you do, do *not* have fun,' remember?"

The sound of helicopter blades disappears.

I make myself smile because I know what Randy wants and I know what my father wants: a lie.

Lying will make them both happy.

"I remember, Dad."

I want to tell him about what I heard in the forest a few sleeps ago and I want to tell him about the boy who turned into a moth and I want to tell him about the trees behind our cabin and how they tried to save me but they couldn't with their feet buried in the dirt. I want to tell him to pick me up and take me away from all this.

I open my mouth to speak but his words come instead.

"I know you only have a couple minutes, Stu, so I'm gonna put your mom on."

"Okay, Dad, I love—"

"—Is this Glenn Stuart?"

He didn't hear me. He didn't hear me at all.

"Hi, Mom."

My mother's voice feels like a warm bath in my own bathtub, in my own house.

"Tell me all about the *fun* stuff you're doing, Glenny"

"Well, we went camping last week up on a mountain."

Randy points to the clock, twirls his finger, *wrap it up.*

"Well, I'm *jealous.* I kinda wish we could trade places, Glenny."

Please. Please trade places with me.

"I know you wish we could trade places, Mom."

I repeat her words to reassure Randy. He smiles, points to the clock again.

"Okay, Mom. I have to get off the phone now."

"What?"

"We only get five minutes."

"That doesn't seem fair."

Nothing does.

"It's so the other kids get a turn."

"Oh, well, that *is* fair then."

"Bye, Mom. I love you."

"Love ya, Glenny."

Why is it so hard to say all three words?

I didn't get an *I love you* from either one of them.

Randy hangs up the phone and tousles my hair and it feels more like an *I love you* than anything I just heard on the phone.

I guess I don't know what love is.

Maybe what Randy does to all of us is love, I don't know. Something inside me feels broken in a way that can't be fixed, and for the first time since I got here, I feel like I wouldn't know how to cry even if I could.

my father's car, one hour later

I want to cry but I can't. I'm too numb, the haze is gone and my eyes are
starting to make sense of the snow and sun outside the windshield. The
memories connecting that snowy intersection to the warmth of my dad's
car right now feel like pictures rotating through another half-empty slide
carousel. I am okay and my father is okay and we are driving home and
that's all that matters.

I focus on my breath as I drive.

In through the nose, out through the mouth.

Over and over and over.

The car smells stale, fleshy, forgotten. An old walk-in freezer.

In through the nose, out through the mouth.

I apologize for making him sit alone for so long in the waiting room and
I tell him about the blood in the bowl this morning and I tell him about
my call to Jay and about skipping my tests and about running away and
getting lost on the streets and he says nothing.

I can't tell if he's pissed or confused or worried, but I suspect *yes*.

Our car hits a long strip of slush on the side of the highway and jerks
toward the shoulder.

"You can't run away from this, Stuie."

I've been running my whole fucking life.

I straighten the car out, put the wipers on full speed to fight off the snow.

"I don't know what's happening to my brain, Pop. Sometimes I feel so
clear. And then, I don't know. I just disappear."

"How often you feel like that?"

"It was more rare a couple months ago but now it feels like it happens every day. Sometimes a few times a day."

"Waitwait, I'm confused. So when you said you were lost at that intersection, were you really lost or were you just thinking about other things?"

"It wasn't like I didn't know who I was, or what city I was in, or *roughly* where I was."

"Okay, good."

"It was like when you and Mom would bring us to the beach when we were little and I'd swim out past the waves and look up a few minutes later and you guys were gone. I'd *eventually* spot you but you were never where I thought you'd be. Or where I thought *I* was. Does that make sense?"

"Yup."

"And I guess the worst part, Pop, is that I don't give a shit. I don't care that I can't find you guys anymore. I'm genuinely fine with letting myself get dragged around by the undertow or whatever the fuck this is. I know that sounds dramatic but it's true. I just don't give a shit."

He lets out a painfully long exhale before he speaks.

"I don't think it's that you *don't give a shit*. I think you're tired. I think you're tired of swimming and I get it. I'm tired too."

He grabs the back of my neck and squeezes it as we coast into his driveway. I turn off the ignition and everything goes quiet. The engine crackles quietly, sporadically, as it settles into the night air.

my father's bedroom, just after midnight

I glance at the clock above the TV and I see that we've just watched over two hours of *Studs*. I know this should feel like the same kind of wasted time I felt circling the hospital parking garage looking for a spot, but somehow it doesn't. It feels warm and still and safe. Almost as if watching these idiots recap their shitty pre-paid dates is somehow slowing time or changing the value of minutes.

"Did Bryce just say, 'I rode that philly into the sunset'? *He* rode *her*?! How the hell is it that we're the ones who wound up with cancer, Pop?"

Silence.

Snoring.

I lean over, kiss his head, tell him goodnight and head back outside to call Jay.

"G?"

His voice is soft with sleep.

"Hey JJ. Sorry for waking you up. I just wanted to tell you that I didn't get the tests done today."

"Why not?"

"Honestly? I don't know. But I'll get them done tomorrow, first thing."

He's annoyed and I don't blame him.

"Night, G."

"Goodnight, JJ. And thank—"

Dial tone.

That's fair.

I slip the phone into my pocket, walk over to Andrea's car, lie down on the hood and stare up at the sky.

There is something so calming in this blackness, in each tiny breath that tumbles out of my mouth and into the hole between the treetops. I love the way they can escape in a way I never could.

I'm starting to think I became two people that night.

I'm the little boy I see in the framed pictures lining the hallway inside: brittle and frail from years of silence, onion-skinned and wounded, arms outstretched and wilted, perpetually trying to connect to something that will never leave me, something that will never hurt me.

I am also the grown man I see in the reflections of mirrors and coffee shop windows and stilled toilet water: numb and distorted, rhino-skinned and scarred, arms outstretched behind a wall of cast iron. Unafraid, reckless, dissociated. With the same little boy locked in the trunk of its car.

I want so desperately to be one person. I want to let that little boy out of the trunk and let him be seen and let him be heard and let him be loved the way I never figured out how to let him be.

A sadness swallows me like the shadow of a hand nearing a flashlight.

my office, two days later

It's late and all of our clients are gone. The bankers, the advertisers, the fashion executives, all the suits are gone. It's just me and a handful of my co-workers working unsupervised.

Technically *I'm* the one being paid to supervise everyone else here, but my boss doesn't know yet what's happened to my brain. He doesn't know just how gone I am.

It's almost midnight and we have been working for twelve hours and I decide I have to require every employee to throw one object out the window of our eleven-story building.

Have to do it.

Part of the job, I decide.

Important part.

We spread out so we each have our own window to poke our heads out of and make sure no one is on the sidewalk below. I tell Dan to go first. A large cup of coffee filled to the brim. The impact of Styrofoam against concrete is glorious and loud and messy.

Goodbye chemo room Ray and your racist fucking mouth.

Troy is next.

He asks if I'm sure we're allowed to do this and I say yes in a way that makes him feel like he's crazy for asking. He leaves and returns with a Tupperware bowl full of old spaghetti, a long-buried orphan from the break room refrigerator.

It lands with a movie-skull pop.

Goodbye greasy fucking pharmacy troll.

The phones ring and I tell everyone to ignore it. I know we're open twenty-four hours, but I actually feel a little annoyed that someone is trying to interrupt us. Frank is getting nervous and asks me if I'm sure we should ignore paying customers.

"Yes I'm sure, Frank. Fuck the phone. It's your turn."

Frank tosses a pad of yellow sticky notes. It floats to the ground as if carried by the hand of a ghost.

We all boo.

Their boos are laughing boos. My boo is angry.

"Find something else, Frank! That sucked."

Frank has been with the company the longest and he is the kind of guy you would trust with your newborn for a month without a check-in call. I love Frank, but whatever the hell has taken over my skull thinks Frank isn't really trying.

"Go get something better, Frank."

His hand shakes as he pushes a mug from the ledge.

A loud pop.

We are all underwhelmed but satisfied.

I look down the row of heads poking out into the night sky and yell *it's Kristine's turn* and that she'd better make it something good. She pulls her head in and we wait. She returns with an open ream of paper, five hundred sheets, and launches it like we all showed up a day late for a ticker-tape parade.

Everyone laughs. I want to laugh but I am hypnotized by the sad beauty of it all, the fluttering chaos, the mess it's leaving on the street below. *Goodbye X-rays, radiology reports, pathology reports, blood tests, goodbye, and fuck off.*

I force myself to laugh because I know it's how they expect me to react and I have to give them the impression that everything inside my brain is intact. It is not.

"Juan! Your turn!"

We all lean out the window and prepare ourselves for another weak Frank-style effort. Juan is sweet and kind and quiet, and I'm sure being forced to participate in this insanity must be hard for him.

He leaves the room and we wait and we wait and we stare at the furthest open window like we're just tuning in to watch a televised zoo birth. Then:

Juan's small hands followed by a fax machine/photocopier the size of a dorm refrigerator.

What the fuck?

The massive chunk of beige equipment drops a couple feet down and stops, suspended and swinging back and forth by its thick industrial power cord. Kristine spots a pedestrian half a block away and calls out to me in a panic. I smile and say nothing.

I am not here.

Frank and Troy call out to Juan and beg him not to let go of the cord and their screams catch the attention of the guy on the street and the guy stops and looks up just as Juan lets go. The impact on the sidewalk sounds like two tractor-trailers in a head-on collision. *A flaming campfire log to your fucking skulls. Goodbye Randy. Goodbye Chuck.*

Glass and plastic and metal shoot off in every direction and the man on the street turns and runs away like there are a hundred more fax machines on the way and Frank is quiet and Troy is quiet and Dan is quiet and Kristine is quiet and Juan is laughing in a way that makes me feel not so alone.

Show's over.

I tell everyone *go home, you've all done good work* and I stick around to clean up the mess on the street below. They each offer to help but I politely decline because I know the mess is mine.

subway, two hours later

I find a corner seat on the subway car as far as physically possible from any other human being and I pull my knees up to my chest, put my head between my legs, tighten them around my ears and lean into this new feeling. The train sways and clicks and hisses and shakes and a yellow square of light on the tunnel wall shoots by quickly and rhythmically over and over. I open my eyes.

I am the only one left in the car.

I am finally alone, but I feel forgotten. I feel like I'm seeing my airplane seatmate across the baggage carousel with his family after we've spent the whole flight talking and laughing together. Like I'm a stranger again. Like I'm on the outside of my own life, and I no longer know what, if anything, is real.

I need to see the sky.

I don't care where I am, I just need to get off at the next stop and see the sky. I need to breathe the night air and smell the passing bodies and see the walls of light spilling from all the stores and bars and restaurants.

The train stops, the bell dings, the doors open. I climb the steps out to the street and I watch my skin change color with the sign lights as I walk.

Blue.

Yellow.

White.

Red.

Purple.

Red.

Bar, market, deli, health clinic, bar, nightclub.
Gone.
I don't care where I am.
A vibration.
Over and over and over.
My phone.
Over and over and over until it stops.
I walk and I start to recognize faces.
This is not my neighborhood but I know these faces.
The same faces. Over and over and over.
A vibration. Over and over and over until it stops.
I walk, smile.
The faces smile back because they know me and they like me and they are happy I am here with them.
A vibration. Over and over and over until it stops.
The faces are happy to see me.
HelloHiHelloHelloHeyHiHelloHiHelloHelloHey
Vibration over and over and over and over and I am smiling and I am walking and the faces are my friends and I love the faces *HelloHiHelloHelloHeyHi* I love you and you love me back *Hello* The vibration in my pocket. Over and over and over.
I love you and you love me back.
Glenn!
I love you and you love me back.
Glenn!
I love you and you love me back.
Pick up the fucking phone!
Hello, I love you and you love me back.
Glenn! Wake up wake up.
"Hello?"
The phone is in my hand, against my ear.
"Glenn?"
GlennGlennGlenn
"This is Glenn."
"Glenn. It's Paisley."
I stop and the light stops and I'm glowing yellow from the Laundromat sign. I am blocking a door and a man is pushing me aside and the sky is black and the air is cold and the vibration has stopped and a voice is bringing me back to the surface.

"Paisley?"

"You okay, Glenn?"

"Yeah yeah, sorry. I don't know. Yeah, I think so."

"I'm sorry to call you so late."

"It's fine. It's good. Paisley, yes yes yes. I'm good, sorry."

"Chris is gone."

Her words are scrambled.

"What?"

"Chris died."

Fuck.

I feel my stomach bubbling up into the back of my throat.

Fuck.

She is crying. I am crying.

A woman brushes my shoulder as she pushes past me.

Then another.

"Was his mother there with you, Paze?"

"No one was there."

"Just you and Chris?"

"*No one* was there."

Paisley is sobbing, trying to catch her breath.

"It. Was. My. Firstdayoff in almost two months."

Chris died alone.

Alone like Corey in the woods. Alone like Owen in the showers.

Something about the image of him dying this way cools my skin the way it gets right before I vomit.

I lean against the building and I breathe. *In through the nose out through the mouth in through the nose out through the mouth.* Paisley's voice fades away as I disappear.

Chris died alone. Chris died without secrets.

day 18

The little white ball against our paddles sounds like a broken clock and
the echo against the ceilings and walls doubles some of the clicks and
makes it so much harder to count.
This is the most I've seen Corey move since he came out of the forest.
There's no net on the ping-pong table and there are freckles of
particleboard where the green parts have chipped off.
It's broken the way everything here is broken.
The sun through the big triangle window high on the wall is painting a
strip of gold where the net should be and I love it because it feels like the
sky is trying to play along with us.
It's me and Corey and the sun and we're all playing ping-pong in a giant
cabin with a high pointed ceiling shaped like the tip of an arrow.
"Your serve, Corey."
It's not Corey's turn and he knows it isn't, but my cheating changes the
shape of his mouth enough for me to see some teeth and that makes
me happy.
It's not a smile but it's close to a smile and close to a smile is enough.
"Eight to six."
Click, clickclick, clickclick.
"Nine to six."
We're not supposed to be here.
We're supposed to be at the pool with the rest of the boys in our cabin
but Randy and Chuck are teaching soccer to a group of older kids and I
know they hate it because Chuck said *we don't get paid enough for this shit*
and Randy said *yeah it's bullshit but Kevin had to leave the camp because he*

busted his shitty ankle.

Watching Corey's thin shiny hair sway back and forth as he dives and stretches for the ball makes me happy.

It's the first time his body hasn't looked dead for a lot of sleeps.

I stopped counting sleeps because each number seemed so far from twenty-four sleeps and it just made me sadder.

"Ten to six. C'mon, Glenn. Try to catch up."

"I'm trying!"

I'm not.

Wood: click, clickclick, clickclick, click, clickclickclick.

Concrete: click ... click ... clickclickclick rollrollrollroll

The ball rolls under the ripped-up couch in the far corner of the room and I run over to get it.

I get on my knees and the cold concrete feels good against my cheek as I look under the couch.

Corey asks if I can see the ball and I tell him *sort of but everything over here smells like horse dick* and he laughs and the sound of his laugh sends a field of dandelions across my skin and it feels so good.

He laughed.

I don't know why *horse dick* is funny, but I heard one of the older boys say it and it made his friends laugh.

Corey walks over and helps me slide the couch away from the wall and he crawls behind it to get closer to the ball.

There are so many spider webs and little pieces of weird old food back there and I feel bad that I didn't offer to crawl back there instead.

"Do you see—?"

BANG.

Flash of sunlight. Thunderclap.

Shitshitshit.

Randy and Chuck are in the doorway. The sun is behind them. They are standing there like the bad guys in an old western movie coming to rob a saloon.

"Glenn!"

Randy says my name like he says the word *bullshit* and it makes my insides feel like firecrackers.

"Hi, Randy!"

I pretend I'm happy to see him and I pretend I'm supposed to be here.

"What the fuck're you doin' here?"

The frozen feeling I had after I got off the phone with my parents takes over again. I'm taller and a different kind of scared now. A kind of scared Randy can see but can't touch.

"I got done swimming and came over here to see if I could find my jawbreaker."

The lie comes so easily. Corey is still behind the couch and I pray he stays there because he's had enough from the lions and I don't mind taking the punishment if it evens up our score like in ping-pong.

Chuck spits a big snot ball onto the floor, laughs, tells Randy I'm lying, tells him to look at my dry hair and my no towel and my no bathing suit.

Randy tells Chuck to shut up and he repeats his question about what the fuck I'm doing here.

I repeat my answer and add more lies.

"Remember I had that big jawbreaker I bought in town? I can't find it and it cost me a dollar fifty and I want it."

"You been lookin' alone?"

"I don't want anyone else to find it."

Randy stares into my eyes in silence as a breeze comes through the door and bends his hair into a hatchet shape.

He looks stupid but I don't laugh. I just stare back.

One, two, three, four, five, six, speak.

"I'm a Jew. I don't want to lose a dollar fifty."

Oh my God. What are you doing?

They both laugh. They both laugh hard.

And as they laugh, I feel like I'm a bird. A giant bird with big sharp claws and huge muscular wings.

I am bigger and stronger and I can fly away anytime I want.

I don't know how long this feeling will last, but I love it so much. For me and for Corey.

Randy turns, shoves Chuck back out the door, says *well, good luck Jew boy, good luck finding your fancy fucking candy*, pulls a cigarette out from behind his ear, lights it, sucks in a bunch of smoke, blows it into the sun and walks away.

The doors squeak and click shut behind him.

I whisper to Corey as I peek out the window.

"Stay there. Lemme make sure they're gone."

Randy and Chuck get smaller and smaller the further down the dirt road they get, and it feels like the good kind of small, like I'm bigger than them even though I know I'm not.

"Okay, it's safe."

Corey pulls himself to his feet using the back of the couch.

His arms and lips and even his eyes are shaking.

He leans against the wall and his breath makes a bouncy sound when he breathes with his eyes closed.

It has the same thump thump thump I feel in the middle of my chest, and the sound makes me feel a whole new kind of sad.

I flop down onto the couch and I tell Corey to sit down next to me until he calms down.

I see that the sun moved its gold bar off the table and onto the wall. I take Corey's paddle out of his hand, bring it over to the ping-pong table, set it down next to mine.

I feel sick.

I feel throw-up sick and I never feel throw-up sick.

I've only thrown up once and that was because I had a fever and strep throat and it was the worst feeling I ever had. I don't like feeling like my body can do something without me telling it to.

My mouth gets wetter and my belly starts tickling.

Shit.

My skin gets cold and wet.

You don't have a fever. You'll be fine.

My legs get wobbly.

Breathe.

I put my hands on the table and my jaw pulls back like it's trying to hide behind me, and my mouth opens and a stream of watery stuff that tastes like tinfoil and old milk shoots out like a fire hose.

It shoots out of my mouth and splashes against the table and it makes a long crackly noise when it hits the wood.

I can't stop it and I get scared that I can't stop it.

I gag and I cough and I spit over and over and over until I have nothing left inside me.

I breathe and I spit and Corey helps me down to the floor and tells me to lie flat on my back and I do.

I stare up at the arrow-shaped ceiling and I see it pointing to the sky like it's some kind of map I should be following.

Breathe.

I want to cry but the tears won't come. I don't like that my body can do something without me telling it to.

cemetery parking lot, new jersey, late morning

I sit and stare at this row of towering evergreens as my black suit soaks up
the heat from the sun flooding through the windshield.
I'm jealous as I watch them.
They're all standing so tall and strong and stoic.
They're alive and everything else is dead.
I'm jealous until I remember they're this way because they're so far from
the edge of the ocean, so far from the saltwater and constant wind.
They're deep-rooted and perfectly vertical because they've never had
to know life any other way. I want to cut their legs off. I really think it
would be the nicest thing I could do for them. Or at least for myself.

graveside, forty-five minutes later

I don't want to waste the time I have left in a place my own body will be soon, but I promised Chris I would. I promised him I would say things to his family that he himself never did, things he wished he had, things he swore he needed them to hear if he was ever going to find peace in this life or wherever he was going next. I agreed to say these things to these people because I saw the despair in his eyes during the hundreds of hours we spent together in his living room alone.

Hours of pain.

The almost-dids and wish-I-hads.

I agreed to say these things even though I know I shouldn't have.

I will say them because I gave Chris my word that I would.

Everyone gathers around the hole in the earth.

The clouds overhead are heavy and oil-stained like old pillows sent to suffocate us. Chris, or what is left of Chris, is hidden behind pine planks and suspended on two blood-red straps, waiting to sink into the earth once certain words have been spoken. There are maybe fifteen of us here in different states of dress, all black, all intended for reverence, even the ponytailed middle-aged man in old white sneakers. I assume this is Roy, the brother who is to receive the brunt of Chris's ire. He nudges a younger blond man standing next to him and lets out a laugh way too loud for a funeral.

That's definitely Roy.

An older man in a dusty charcoal-colored suit clears his throat.

"I wanna say something before we get started with the official stuff ..."

Chris's father, Max.

The pastor nods his approval even though Max clearly wasn't asking permission.

"… I know you're not supposed to speak bad of the dead but I can't lie. I'm not a liar. And I'm not gonna say a bunch of nonsense about Chris just because he's dead."

His eyes redden and it's hard to say if he's pissed or sad.

"So I'm just gonna say it: Chris was a difficult kid and he was even harder as he grew up. He was *different*. Everyone said so. 'Chris is different' is what they *all* said—even some of you—and I knew what that meant. We *all* knew what that meant. And that's why I couldn't cry when he got sick and I don't wanna cry now. He's dead because he made a choice to go against God's will . . ."

The pastor shifts uncomfortably, clearly deciding whether he should interrupt or not. He doesn't.

". . . so let's not all say a bunch of bullshit about my son just 'cause it's the right thing to do. I mean it. Just speak your mind 'cause that's all Chris deserves. In my opinion, anyways."

On my drive over here, I kept trying to talk myself out of reading aloud the words Chris asked me to read. I even found a way to soften them so they wouldn't sound so angry.

Don't do it, Glenn.

Roy pats his father on the back.

Do not speak.

"I think what my dad is sayin' is that my brother had an opinion about everything and we should honor him by speakin' the truth."

Max nods. A petite old woman shaped like a question mark stands glued to Max's side and cries like she's afraid to be seen crying, like she's afraid to be seen.

Chris's mom, Ruth.

Ruth is the only one in Chris's family who ever came to visit him. And even though I never met her, I know he struggled with being both grateful for her visits and hurt that she only visited secretly.

Seeing his family now, I can see why.

I want to run over and pick her up like she's a shelter dog, drive her away and find her a loving home to live out the rest of her days.

The pastor recites several prepared passages from a book of old poetry and finishes with a rehearsed story that invokes a full cast of biblical heavyweights.

Chris would hate this.

He asks us to add any final words we may want to share.

Leaveleaveleave. Don't speak.

Paisley raises her hand sheepishly as if she's back in grade school.

"I was Chris's nurse for a long time …"

Her voice shakes as she holds back her tears.

"… and I'll really miss him. He was a gentle soul and he always made me laugh. And he didn't really have much to joke about."

Roy chuckles, speaks in a stage whisper.

"Are we talkin' about the same Chris?"

Paisley smiles politely and takes a step backward as if she suddenly wishes she were invisible. Roy looks around with a self-important grin on his face like he's challenging anyone else to speak up.

Don't speak don't speak don't speak.

He signals to the pastor to wrap it up and I feel a shift inside me, the same twisting feeling I felt at work the other night, that hunger to destroy ordinary things.

Don't don't don't.

"I'm sorry. I just have to say a few words because I told Chris I would."

Fuck it. This is for you, Chris.

"I know none of you know me, but I was a friend of Chris's and he wanted me to say a few words on his behalf. He made me promise him I would, and I'm a man of my word, so here goes."

I pull the folded piece of paper from my breast pocket. I address Mom first and I tell her Chris forgives her and I tell her that her husband is a tyrant and a bigot and I tell her she did the best she could and that Chris loves her.

Fasterfasterfaster.

I tell Dad that Chris hopes one day he will realize that God only wants people to love each other and that God doesn't care whether those people are men or women or both. I remind Dad that Chris fell apart when he stopped talking to him. I tell him that Chris put himself back together and he hopes maybe Dad will realize one day that he and Chris are very much alike and maybe it's just that Dad doesn't want to acknowledge certain parts of himself.

There is a stir in the air and people shift and I know I am too far in to stop. And now I don't want to stop.

I want to say everything out loud to everyone, for everyone.

I want to say everything out loud to everyone, for myself.

My hand shakes as I make my way down the note.

I tell Roy that Chris will never forgive him, that the words Roy used to tear Chris down were the meanest and hardest to hear, made worse coming from his own brother. I tell him AIDS isn't a punishment from God for the lifestyle Chris led because if that were true, Roy himself would already be dead.

Oh shit.

I look at Max and Ruth.

"Ask your son Roy over there about a man named Phillip."

Holy fucking shit.

Roy's face turns the color of an old stop sign.

He tells me *that's enough, that's enough.* I believe he'd choke me to death with his bare hands right now if he could.

That's enough, Glenn. This isn't your fight. Congratulations though. You're a fucking hero. You're giving Chris a voice in death while maybe giving yourself a death in life. Just shut up. You've done enough.

I look at the pastor, tell him there is only one sentence left.

He stares at me in silence and I finish with the only part of the note I have memorized.

"You have two gay sons and one of them is a liar."

Silence.

Fuckfuckfuck.

I know this was a mistake but this bell has been rung and I have kept my word.

That was for you, Chris. Fuck your brother.

I fold the paper, slip it back into my pocket, weave my way out of the crowd, march up a hill of scattered headstones, follow the paved road back to the parking lot, get into my car and drive. I am mad at myself for keeping my word. I am mad at myself for being there. I am mad at myself for trying to fool myself into believing that this was ever just about Chris. I am mad at myself for publicly shaming a family I didn't know instead of shaming my own family. I am mad at myself for thinking my own family *needs* to be shamed. Especially for something from my childhood that they don't even know exists. I am mad at myself for speaking someone else's truth. I am mad at myself for believing, even for a second, that I am courageous for doing it. I am a fucking coward with my own truth. A truth I'm too afraid to tell the people I love.

It's easier to be brave with someone else's pain.

I want to call Jen and tell her I'm sorry for being here today, tell her I'm sorry for not staying home today with her and Danny. I want to call her and feel her words wrap themselves around me in forgiveness and understanding. I want to call her, but I don't. I call my father instead.

"Did you actually do it, Stuie?"

"Yeah."

He sighs.

I know he's disappointed.

"That wasn't fair. Or kind. Plus, it's not really like you ..."

I feel my face heat up.

"That said, Stuie, it's a pretty beautiful fuck-you to his brother."

I laugh, a tiny moment of relief.

"Thanks Dad. I feel horrible."

"You shouldn't. You're like Braveheart for the gays."

"*The gays*—"

"I'm kidding, Stu. I'm just trying to lift some of the weight
off you. I know how hard it was for you to do that for him."

"It *was* terrible. But it's over."

It's over.

doctor's office, the next day

Jay's waiting room is depressing even for an oncologist's office, everything a combination of beige and deep brown. The tables, the chairs, the lamps, the wallpaper, the carpet. It's like a giant colon.

I don't usually have to sit in the waiting room, but Jay has three patients in three different exam rooms and I don't have the luxury of bypassing everything the way I do in the wee hours of the morning, the private hours, the hours he sets aside for himself that I've thoughtfully invaded and destroyed over the past few months.

The only other person in the waiting room is a thin, frightened-looking blonde girl in her early twenties. She's skimming through a copy of *People* that looks like it's been here for decades.

I clear my throat and speak.

"There's a great profile in there on Mamie Eisenhower. Seems like she's gonna make a great First Lady."

She looks up. Her eyes erase me. I know those eyes. Wide, wet, terrified. The eyes all of us have. The eyes of a rat in a maze with no idea what new horror lies around the next corner. I want to walk over and hold her and let her know that everything is going to be okay even though I have no idea if it will.

If it ever will.

She speaks.

"I haven't gotten to that article yet—"

She didn't get my shitty joke.

"—but I just finished a story about that Inquisition thing going on in Spain."

I love her.

I walk across the waiting room and I sit three chairs away. She laughs at my seat choice, speaks through a smile.

"Cancer's not contagious."

I feel a rush of blood to my face.

"I just didn't want you to think I was a rapist or a murderer or something."

Idiot.

"That's very thoughtful of you."

"You're welcome."

She smiles and puts her palm against her chest, *I'm Shelly.*

"Glenn!"

Settle down, idiot.

She laughs, tells me I seemed much more confident on the other side of the room. I walk back to my original seat, tell her I'm sorry for being so awkward.

Jay pops his head through the receptionist's sliding glass window.

"Hey G. I can get you into a room in a minute. You can wait in my office if you want."

"I'm fine, JJ. Take your time."

He cranes his neck, sees Shelly, says hello, disappears.

She turns to me and smiles.

"You guys are on a first-name basis, huh?"

"We're lovers."

She gives me an unamused courtesy smile.

"I'm sorry. I probably *am* better from a distance."

"Yeah, kinda. What's your prognosis, Glenn?"

"It was Stage IV when they found it and now we're just waiting to see if the clinical trial I just finished bought me more time. You?"

She laughs the way I do when I don't want to answer a question.

"Well it started off better than where it wound up."

"Meaning?"

She tells me her original prognosis was good, assuming she did the surgery, chemo and radiation, and that she could live a relatively long and normal life after she got through the worst of it.

"I sense a '*but*' coming."

"Yeah, a big '*but.*' I guess it spread to my bones and now I'm having some kind of other issue with my skin hardening or something."

"Not from the radiation?"

"Nope. A mutation of the cancer or whatever. Apparently, all they can do now is make me *comfortable*."

An ocean wells up behind her eyes and the effort she's making to hold it in makes me tear up. She sees my tears and hers come hard and fast. I walk over, wrap my arms around her and let her cry into my shirt. Her chest feels rigid and squared off like a CPR dummy, her arms atrophied and frail. She lets out a howl I recognize from my own heart. The howl of a new life clawing to stay tethered to its womb.

Too young, too young, too fucking young.

Too young the way I was then. Too young the way I am now.

"I have an idea, Shelly."

She speaks into my shirt.

"What's that?"

"Let's do a Thelma and Louise thing. Fuck it, right?. We're both dying."

"I don't remember what that movie was about."

"Me neither but they drive off a cliff at the end."

"Were they dying?"

"Probably at that moment, yeah."

I'm trying to make light of the pain, but I find myself falling in love instead, or what feels like falling in love, fast and electric and all-consuming, and I want this moment with Jen, not a stranger, but a stranger is all I have right now. All I can give is a love that requires no maintenance, an anonymous love, an understanding love, a confused displaced love, a dying love, a love with a finish line and an expiration date.

The feeling of holding Shelly in my arms now, this wounded bird left to die on a skyscraper ledge, how I feel in my own skin every single day. There is nothing ahead of us and there is nothing behind us and this feeling of presence doesn't feel good the way people say it should. This feels like *Fuck It All* presence. Fuck sick, fuck happy, fuck fatherhood, fuck fidelity. Fuck commitments made on paper, commitments made on an illusion of what the world expects. Fuck my job, fuck my friends, fuck my parents, fuck my doctors, fuck my nurses, fuck everyone who is not here now, fuck everyone who is not dying and not terrified, fuck everyone who is not Shelly, fuck everyone who is not me, fuck everyone and everything, fuck everyone and everything that doesn't feed this moment, this new brain, these new thoughts, these new eyes, this new reality, small and frozen and indestructible, fuck everything, fuck everything but *This*, fuck everything but *Now*.

We are alive and we are in love and we will never let go.

Two minutes three minutes four minutes five minutes six minutes seven minutes eight minutes nine ten eleven twelve.

Jay opens the door and sees us hugging.

"Interesting ..."

Shelly lets go and winces as she sits back down.

"G, let's get you in a room."

I tell him to take Shelly first, remind him that I'm a *goddamn gentleman.*

I help her into the open exam room, go back to the waiting room, sit and stare at the cover of some new-age magazine. It's a picture of a single votive candle in a dark room. I want to run back into Shelly's room and tell her to hang on, tell her not to leave this planet, tell her that the same wind that could blow out this stupid fucking candle is the same wind that could keep a wildfire burning forever. And that maybe we'll both get the latter.

Jay opens the door, hands me a small stack of papers, tells me to call the numbers on the letterhead and schedule more scans.

"Shelly's appointment is gonna take a while and I don't want you to wait."

"I don't mind waiting, JJ."

"Until you get these other scans, there's nothing new I can tell you anyway, G."

I hug him and I ask him to please save Shelly's life.

He tells me to go home, tells me to go home to my wife and my baby boy.

I'm not ready to go home.

park avenue, forty-five minutes later

I lean against the frozen concrete legs of the building across the street
from Jay's office and I wait for Shelly to make her way out. I have no idea
what I'm going to do when I see her or even if I'll do or say anything.
I guess right now I'm just enjoying the sting of the cold night air, the
hyphenated blare of car horns, the sight of moths circling the caged
lightbulb over the service entrance of the corner apartment building.
I know I must look crazy standing out here in the cold, but I don't care.
I feel oddly free, oddly not myself.
A buzz in my coat pocket.
Mom's phone.
I flip mine open, speak through my chattering jaw.
"Hi Ma."
"I'm not your mother. But I *can* be for the right price."
Ronnie.
Ronnie has a rolling list of hackneyed jokes that he cycles through several
times a day. It's usually met with strangers' eye-rolls or courtesy laughs
or confusion.
I find it charming. It feels like the language of a dying generation.
Every waiter and waitress gets stopped with the same "if you see a Diet
Coke walking around, could you ask it to stop by our table?" Any host or
hostess who asks, "Is this table okay?" will invariably get an "Oh, we're
not proud, just desperate."
Anytime he's asked for his last name, he gives the standard "It's Briskman.
Brisk-Man. As in 'Fast Fellow'."
He always introduces me as his "less-handsome son" and depending on

how well it's received, "the son I sleep with."

A line that's never well-received.

I love all the lines. The more twisted, the better.

"Hey Ronnie. What's going on?"

"Your mother and I are just checking in on you."

My mom chimes in with a *Hi Sweetie* on the other line.

"I just left Jay's office. He ordered a couple scans I'll need to get in the next few days."

An older Black man in a wool peacoat opens the front door of Jay's building and holds it open for Shelly. My heart quickens as I watch her thin silhouette shuffle across the icy sidewalk.

"Hey guys, lemme call you back."

"Is it something we said?"

Another Ronnie-ism.

I hang up, search for a break in the river of headlights streaming downtown, run to the center median, search for a break in the taillights flowing uptown. I cup my hands around my mouth and try to yell louder than the traffic.

"Shelly!"

I stand there marooned between the glowing red and white rivers as she flags down a cab and I watch her ease herself into the back seat with a wince. *Too fucking young.* I open my phone and call my dad as I watch Shelly disappear into the rush.

I need to see him.

my father's car, the next day

The sky is the color of wet ashes, only slightly darker than the shade
of my father's skin. We're driving through the side streets of his
neighborhood as he tries to direct me through the fog of his eyes
and memory.

"Take a right up here, Stuie."

We're lost but I don't care because we are alone and we are talking.
I love this time together.

A part of me believes that if I can just keep driving then we can keep
talking and we can stop dying and I can keep telling him all the things
I need him to hear.

"Your appointment's early tomorrow, Pop."

"Yeah. It wasn't his fault."

What?

He's been getting confused today for some reason. I don't know if he's
tired or scared or medicated or feverish or all of these things, but these
moments are peeling away parts of me that I know I will never get back.
The snow starts to fall. The quiet it brings, calms me.

"Talked to your uncle last night, Stuie."

"How's he holding up?"

My aunt was recently diagnosed with breast cancer and is preparing
for surgery.

"Pretty good, all things considered. He asked me a bunch of questions
about my treatment and if it was working and all that."

"What'd you tell him?"

He points to the snow-dusted stop sign at the end of the block.

"You're gonna turn left up there. I told him … well, I was honest with him. He knows I'm not doing so well."

"Jesus. It's gotta be rough on him to have his brother, his nephew and his wife going through this all at the same time."

"Take a left after that red house."

I've taken that same left turn three times already but there's something about talking without making eye contact that makes this all a little easier.

"Was it hard to talk about all this with him?"

"Nah. I didn't mind it actually. Made me feel less lonely in a weird way."

My mind starts to drift alongside the falling snow. I know the loneliness he's describing all too well.

I think about last night. Jen and I awake and in bed, Danny fast asleep between us, the glow of the nightlight against the ceiling, softening all the words we weren't saying, all the words I wish we were saying. Me not talking about how scared I am or how much I need her or how pathetically jealous I am of the love she showers on Danny. Her not talking about how scared she is or how much she wishes I hadn't retreated into myself or how pathetically jealous she is of the love I shower on Danny. Both of us together, alone.

My father's forehead wrinkles as he runs his hand through his hair. A mad scientist clawing his way through a tiny universe inside his head.

"It's like … I don't know, a loneliness where every single second you're—"

He stops himself, grins.

"I don't know what the hell I'm saying."

"It's fine. I think I get it, Pop."

"I don't know how you *could*, Stu. I feel like I'm knocking on a bunch of rooms with no doors."

I don't know what he means by this but I smell the blood of his confusion in the water and I lunge.

"I've been lonely since I was seven years old, Pop."

"What?"

"Since you dropped me off at that fucking camp. Seven years old and left alone with strangers for almost a goddamn month. *Monsters*, Pop. They were fucking monsters. And you and Mom wonder why I was so different when you picked me up."

"A bunch of rooms with no doors, Stuie."

What? He didn't hear a word. He's somewhere else.

He continues without explaining.

"Right before we hung up, your uncle asked me how I get through it all. Like how I get through the chemo and the feeling crappy and the being scared and the planning my own funeral and all that."

A car flies through the intersection right in front of us and I slam on the brakes and the back of our car fishtails into a snowbank.

He's completely unfazed in a way that makes me wonder if he even registered any of it. I stay silent as the adrenaline in my bloodstream slowly dissipates.

We make several trips through the same ten blocks and eventually I try to pick up where we left off.

"He wants to know how you get through it? You can tell him he can ask *me* too. I may actually die before you."

"Might."

"Oh, sorry. I *might* actually die before you."

"Might."

"Yeah, I heard you."

He stares out the windshield in silence. Several minutes pass before he finally speaks.

"No. That was my answer: *might*."

My eyes well up as I realize his beautiful brain is dying and I can't do a fucking thing to save it. I drive us home through the falling snow and we say nothing. This was now a conversation we never had. He didn't hear a word of what took me a goddamn lifetime to say.

my father's bedroom, that night

I'm on the floor next to the bed staring at the veins of rust on the ceiling
and listening to the ebb and flow of my father's breath.
The red glow of the alarm clock reads *2:18 a.m.,* and another sun is gone.
I give his breath enough time to find its deepest rhythm before I allow
myself to leave.
There it is.
He's asleep.
I creep downstairs, bundle up, gently close the front door behind me.
My breath starts to stream out of my mouth like it's been packed with
dry ice.
I walk and I breathe and I try to quiet my mind. There's a heartbeat
underneath the snow. This neighborhood has a life I can feel only at this
time of night, the time of night when every light in every window has
been turned off and replaced with the electricity of dreams I imagine
must be unfolding in all of those happy, un-dying, secret-less minds.
Fuck off, Glenn.
I hate these thoughts.
I hate this heightened sense of victimhood that's been creeping in more
and more over the last few weeks. I am dying. I will die. My dad will die.
We will die. We will *all* die. I am not a victim and I am not unique and
I am not special. I'm just a mammal. I eat, shit, feel, endure, survive,
decay, die, rot. I didn't invent death no matter how much my terrified
brain wants to try to convince me I did.
Keep walking, keep breathing. And shut the fuck up.

The snowplows have turned the sidewalks into foxholes and I love how muffled my feet sound as I walk. I inhale, exhale, feel my heart settle to the rhythm of my footsteps. As I amble through the hills and half-tunnels, I think about how quickly he's thinning out up there in that bedroom. I think about how my days will change if he survives, how they will change if I survive. For me and for the people around me.

I can't erase the sight of the blood and vomit and piss and shit and the bits of my mouth that sloughed off under the flow of chemicals that coursed through my veins and I know I can't erase the rotting stench of it all because it lives with me now. Every second of every day. Asleep or awake.

A clump of snow falls from the arm of a pine tree and hits my arm.

What the fuck?!

The impact sends a jolt through me like a zap from the third rail.

I can't catch my breath.

What the fuck was that?

Corey's desperate whimpers from deep in the woods, my legs frozen like tree roots, Randy's sandpaper paw clutching my jaw and forcing my eyes toward his.

I can't catch my breath.

Fuckfuckfuck.

Shelly's paper-thin arms clinging to my chest, the terror in my dad's eyes, green-to-black, Jen's paper-thin heart buried helpless in her chest, Danny's melting chocolate eyes oblivious to the Mack truck speeding toward his crib.

I stop and I lean against the snowbank and I try to take a deep breath but my heart starts to pound faster when I can't remember how.

I take out my phone, tilt it in the direction of the streetlamp, call Jay.

It goes right to voicemail.

Fuckfuckfuck.

I heave, start to guppy-breathe, grab the snow with both hands, squeeze it into hard clumps, close my eyes and try to remember how to breathe.

I put my hand against my heart, rub it, tell it *it's safe to relax*, tell it *you're not going to die. It's okay it's okay it's okay. That bulb is a lie, stop circling, look up look up look up, follow the fucking moon, where's the fucking moon?*

Silence.

I take in a full breath and it fills my lungs.

I can't do this.

This is the kind of *new* I worry about.

I can't do this.
Snow from a tree. That's all it took.
A touch I never chose, a touch I couldn't control.
I can't do this.
Snow from a fucking tree.
I know my body will never be able to sustain itself if this is how it will feel any time it gets blindsided by gravity.
I stand up and I count my breaths as I walk.
I'm teaching myself how to breathe again.
Snow from a fucking tree.
It's time to go home.

It's time to go home.

Randy is pacing back and forth across the cabin, running his fingers through his hair over and over like he's worried about something. It's weird to see him wearing a collared shirt and shoes that aren't flip-flops. It's like he's trying to hide.

He's pacing like a lion, but now he looks like my neighbor's cat.

It doesn't make me feel any more comfortable to see him small and weak like this because I know it's a lie.

"Your folks are gonna start showing up soon so make sure you got all your shit packed up and you didn't leave anything behind."

I feel sad for Randy. He really *does* look scared.

More like the rest of us now.

Or like there's a lion bigger than him somewhere that he's afraid of.

He stops in front of the small mirror next to the door and he finger-fluffs his hair and smooths out his new mustache with his thumb and finger and talks to us through the reflection.

"We all had fun, didn't we?"

It sounds like one of those questions grown-ups ask where they get mad if you give them an answer.

Owen says *No* like he can't stop it from coming out of his mouth.

Randy turns around like he's big again, and even though the air feels scary, it also feels like there's an invisible wall in the middle of the cabin that stops him from touching us.

The big iron bell in the middle of camp starts to ding, a sound that usually means it's time to eat.

We already had breakfast and breakfast was supposed to be our last meal before our parents get here.

Randy walks less tough and his voice is softer as he walks out the door. "I gotta give your parents a tour around the place before I bring 'em up here to get you guys. Until then, you stay on your bunks and do quiet shit. I don't wanna find anything outta place when I get back."

He slams the door behind him and we all sit quietly and wait for the thumpy sound of Randy's normal shoes clomping down the steps to disappear. It's weird not hearing that sticky click of his flip-flops.

I start counting.

It feels good to count because I know that when I stop counting my mom and dad will be here and I will be done with this.

Corey gets up from his bunk. Mark whispers *what the heck are you doing* and Corey ignores him.

I beg Corey to get back on his bunk but he's already in Randy's room sifting through the junk Chuck left on the windowsill.

No no no.

He walks back into the room and his face looks like someone else is operating his body with a remote control from somewhere far away.

Forty-two.

His eyes are wide and black and his face is frozen in a crooked smile.

Fifty-nine.

It's the same look I saw on my next-door neighbor's face last summer when he sat up in his bedroom window and shot his own dad in the neck with a bb gun while his dad was mowing the lawn.

Corey walks back into the room with a red plastic cup, unzips his fly and starts to pee into it as we all watch in silence.

Eighty-eight.

Owen lets out a weird-sounding laugh and it makes all of us laugh even though our laughs sound weird now too.

One hundred sixty-two.

Corey zips his fly back up, drags his camp trunk to the door, stands on top of it, cracks the door open just enough to set the cup of pee on top of it and lean it against the frame.

Two hundred eleven, oh my God, two hundred twelve.

He drags the trunk back, sits on his bunk and folds his arms across his belly like he's been sitting there the whole time.

Two hundred forty-seven, oh my God oh my God oh my God, two hundred fifty.
I hear Randy's voice in the distance.
"I'll go round up your boys and meet you folks down by the stable."
Two hundred seventy-seven.
He's coming back alone.
Two hundred ninety-two oh my God three hundred one.
He's coming back alone.
Three hundred seventeen.
I stop counting as Randy clomps back up the stairs.
Corey stands next to his bed, grabs the leather handle of his trunk, stares at the door and waits there stiff and tall like a middle finger.
Clomp clomp squeek.
The door flies open.
Pop.
Splash.
The cup falls, hits Randy's shoulder, splashes against his face, crashes to the floor and bounces to a slow roll.
He's covered in piss and he's frozen with rage and he's breathe-spitting like he just lifted his head out of a cold pool.
Silence.
Threads of spit and urine drip from his chin and fall to the floor. They make a weird crackly sound when they hit the wood.
I feel nothing.
Corey drags his trunk across the floor, kicks the cup, tries to push his way out the door.
Randy refuses to move.
Corey screams *Dad* even though I don't think his dad is anywhere nearby.
He tries again.
"Hey, Dad!"
Randy steps aside.
Corey drags his trunk down the steps and onto the dirt road and keeps walking. He never turns around. He never looks back.
Randy starts talking again.
"The rest of you guys can grab your stuff and head down to the flagpole area."
His voice is flat, like he didn't just get hit with a cup of hot pee.
For some reason this makes me feel bad for him even though he doesn't deserve the nice part of me or the nice part of anyone.

I stand, say *thanks for everything Randy,* drag my own trunk down the
steps and start walking toward the center of camp.

The sky is different today.

It's gray and foggy and cold and it feels more like winter than summer.

And even though it does, I feel warmer than I did all those other days
when the sun was out all day.

Corey is too far ahead of me and I can't see him through the fog and it
feels like my friend is a ghost now.

boston train station, late morning

Another sun is here. It's hidden behind the clouds but it's here.
We stand on the train platform and my father holds my backpack like it's
my first day of school and he's here to make sure I get settled onto the
bus safely. I cinch my jacket tighter against my neck and I speak.
"I wish I could go to your appointment with you this morning, Pop."
He shivers, marches in place.
"I'm glad you can't."
"What? Why?"
"Every time you come with me, you wind up wanting to strangle the guy."
"I *do* want to strangle him!"
"I know, Stuie. But you have to remember that all you need your doctor to
do is get you the things that give you the best shot at beating this thing.
It doesn't matter if you like him or not."
"I know, Pop. But just on a human level ... the guy can at least burn the
calories to *act* like he gives a shit, right?"
He laughs softly, the way someone who has spent a lifetime
deconstructing, dissecting and scrutinizing every nuance of human
behavior would.
"That's just your narcissism, Stu."
A man walks by holding an enormous golf umbrella and it hits the side of
my dad's face.
What the fuck.
I smack it out of the guy's hand reflexively. It falls onto the platform and
gets dragged away by the wind before getting stopped by the trash bin
bolted to the concrete.

He turns and yells.

"What the hell was that for!"

I want him to see me. I want him to see that I'm bigger than lions now.

"Get a normal-sized umbrella, you prick."

"Screw *you*."

A maniacal smile comes to my face as I start walking and my father grabs my arm. *Too late to protect me now, Dad.*

"I'm gonna shove that fucking—"

My father pipes up.

"—I'm sorry. My son has special needs."

He walks over, picks up the man's umbrella, hands it back to him with another *I'm sorry*.

The man shakes his head in disgust and I yell at the back of his head as he walks away.

"There are other fucking people on this planet, dickhead."

"Glenn Stuart!"

Shit. Both names.

I turn and my eyes sigh when I see how stressed he looks.

"I'm sorry."

"Stuie, listen …"

I look into his eyes. There's a catastrophic sadness holding those yellowing whites and dulling greens.

"This narcissism. This rage. This hair-trigger? These are all just the leftovers. Being so goddamn sick, just *having* cancer … *that's* the real monster. All this other stuff is just its ghost."

The train is coming.

"Try putting your energy into killing *that*. It's really not fair to make the world pay for something they can't see."

Something you *can't see either, Dad.*

The train thunders in and erases the rest of his words and I know they don't matter because I know he's right. It's not fair to make anyone else pay for something that was never theirs, something they can't see.

I take my backpack from him, hold him, kiss the side of his head over and over and tell him I love him.

He holds my face in his gloves and tells me to kill the monster and silence the ghost. He has no idea how many ghosts I've spent my life trying to silence, but he's right. I'm bigger than lions now and I'm definitely bigger than their ghosts.

the train back to manhattan, twenty minutes later

BuildingTreesBuildingTreesHouseHouseTreesHouse. Strange and familiar
flying by my window. This world between my death and his death
is a blurry backdrop that feels like a Hollywood prop designed to
give the illusion of distance and time. I'm hypnotized by the pattern.
BuildingTreesTreesHouseTreesTunnelTunnelTunnel.
The tunnel turns my window to a temporary mirror and I catch a
reflection of my pathetic face. My nose, cheekbones and chin jutting out
and fish-eyed under my pale vinyl skin.
I hate what I see.
I scan the rest of the reflection for distractions and I spot the umbrella
guy a couple rows down on the other side of the aisle.
Go apologize, Glenn.
I stand and step into the aisle.
Stop stop stop. He can't see what you see.
You're right, Dad.
This man isn't the monster and he's not its ghost.
I sit back down, breathe.
My phone vibrates. A number I don't recognize.
"G?"
I can't place the woman's voice, but I respond anyway.
"G's a good start—but what're the other letters?"
She laughs, starts to cough.
"Are you okay, whoever you are?"
I hear a weak smile in her voice.
"Not really, but that's okay."

A greasy-haired guy in a Patriots jersey walks out of the bathroom and drags an unholy stench along with him as he makes his way back to his seat. I cover my nose with my shirt as she speaks.

"It's Shelly."

"Hi Shelly!"

Shelly? Who's Shelly?

"You sound like you're not sure you if remember me, Glenn."

"Not true! I'm *totally* sure I don't remember you ..."

She laughs herself into a coughing storm and I wait for it to settle before I continue.

"... I'm sorry. Remind me, Shelly."

"I'm the crying terminal girl you hugged for ten minutes in Jay's waiting room."

How the hell did I forget Shelly?

My brain is starting to erase the wrong things.

"Oh my God, I'm so sorry, Shelly! How're you doing?"

"Still terminal!"

I laugh hard, ask how she got my number.

"You wrote it on my colostomy bag."

I love her.

"I can barely hear you, Glenn."

I pull the shirt off my face, explain that I'm on the train and that I'm talking through my shirt to save me from the stench of the gross dump the guy dragged out with him from the bathroom.

"That's fun."

Nice job, Glenn.

"Anyway, Glenn. I'm calling because I wanted to know if you could swing by the hospital at some point soon. I could really use the distraction."

"Of course. But I haven't seen my wife and son in a couple days, so how about Thursday?"

"Can you come by tonight?"

Fuck. I recognize the sound of that question mark.

I ask for the address and I tell her I'll head over as soon as my train gets in and she sounds more relaxed when she says thank you.

I miss her so much.

I miss Shelly and I love her and it's okay that she can't show me how much she loves me or how scared she is to lose me. It's okay because she's human. She's loved me unconditionally and I've loved her just as fiercely. It's easy to forgive her reticence and her distance. She's human and she's terrified of what's coming her way. She loves me and she needs me and I will never abandon her.

I miss you, Jen.

Yes. Jen, yes, Jen Jen Jen.

I lean over, put my head in my free hand and tell Shelly—*Shelly*—that I'll bring her a gift when I come. She warns me that her grandparents will be there. She knows my twisted brain well enough already.

She sees me and she knows me and she loves me the way only an illusion or a fantasy can.

I miss her so much.

I lean my head against the cold window and it feels good against my hot skin. I close my eyes and fall asleep.

penn station, nyc, four hours later

I have to walk through Times Square to catch the subway line that will take me to the hospital, so I duck into a sex shop and ask the man at the high checkout counter where I can find the largest dildo in the city. He asks me how much I want to spend and I tell him *whatever it takes* because I'm dying of cancer and I'm putting everything on a credit card anyway.

His eyes light up and he tells his short, sweaty coworker by the door to show me where the dildos are and then tells him something in another language I assume has to do with making sure I see the good stuff.

My new guide motions to a row of glass display cases along the back wall. I notice that the glass on each case is cracked and taped up with clear packing tape.

"How desperate does someone have to be to kick open a dildo display case?"

Nothing.

Just shut up and get the hell out of here, Glenn

The man pulls a small key from his retractable keychain and opens the case like it's the Ark of the Covenant. He reaches in, pulls out a two-foot double-sided dildo, sets it on the counter.

"One-hundred sixty-five dollars. Plus tax."

You can't afford that.

"I'll take it!"

He looks pleasantly surprised and I'm guessing I do too.

He carries it to the front desk and I give him my credit card and he tries to bend the dong into a black plastic bag.

"It's fine. I'll just carry it."

I sign the receipt, tuck the dildo under my arm like a baguette, walk to the subway station, pack myself into the nearest car, sway and wobble with the movement of the train as it barrels uptown.

I walk into the hospital and tell the white-haired man behind the counter that I'm here to see Shelly.

He looks down at his chart and he speaks without looking up.

"Your name?"

"Glenn Rockowitz."

He picks up a phone the same color as the bouncy gift under my arm.

"Gland Marskwich."

Wow. Didn't even try.

He puts the phone back into its cradle and he points toward the hallway to his left and tells me the room number.

I thank him and I walk to Shelly's room and I tap on the half-open door with one knuckle.

An adorable elderly woman in a cream-colored sweater and high-waisted pink slacks opens the door and motions for me to come in.

I hold my index finger to my lips to let her know I'll be quiet.

I notice Shelly's not in her bed.

Great. I suck at small talk.

Several people, who I assume are family members, are standing quietly in different spots throughout the room.

I start to sweat.

You need to leave, Glenn.

A middle-aged man with dark brown hair graying at the temples extends his hand and introduces himself as Shelly's father. He tells me she's in the restroom with her nurses.

The room is painfully silent and reverent in a way that tells me there's no way these people are Jewish. I don't do well with tense silence but I can hear my father's voice telling me to "read the room."

Say nothing. Say nothing. Say nothing.

A bead of sweat falls from my armpit and slides down my ribcage.

Say nothing. You'll only screw this up.

Shelly's father finally breaks the silence.

"So, you're the new boyfriend."

Huh?

I feel my face heat up.

"Uhh … yup, yup. New boyfriend."

Why the hell would Shelly tell him that?

"She tells us you two met at the oncologist's office."

"Yeah. Right there. I met her right … there."

You're doing great, Glenn.

I wipe the sweat from my upper lip. The only sound in the room is the tick of the wall clock.

Tick.

Tick.

Tick.

Toilet flush.

Finally.

The bathroom door opens and everyone turns to watch the nurses escort Shelly back to her bed. The bathroom light creates a silhouette of her brittle body through the white gown. She stares at her feet as she shuffles. She doesn't notice I'm in the room. The nurses adjust her, get her upright and comfortable, and one of them holds a plastic cup to her mouth as Shelly fumbles to find the straw with her open lips. Her hands are shaking too much to hold the cup herself. She takes a small sip and she winces.

I hate this.

She looks so different from the last time I saw her. It wasn't even that long ago, but her eyes have retreated and her lips have thinned and her neck has tightened.

Fuck all of this.

I turn and I look out the window and I watch the clouds slide across the gunmetal sky as I try to slow my pulse.

Stars?

I see a couple stars.

Two three four five six seven stars, in through the nose out through the mouth, eight nine ten eleven stars, in through the nose out through the mouth, twelve stars.

Shelly leans forward and scans the room with her pale green eyes.

She's too out of it.

I should've just gone home.

I should've just gone home to my real wife and my real son and my real family.

Her head pans slowly.

There she is.

Her eyes go wide and a lightness falls over her and she smiles.

She's still here.

"Hi honey."

Her words catch me off guard.

"Hi Shells. I thought you might not remember me."

"Whatcha got there, honey?"

I forgot that I've been standing here with this giant dildo tucked under my armpit.

Goddammit.

"Oh. This? Yeah. I got this for you."

Shelly's father opens the door and announces he's going to give us some time alone and suggests everyone else join him. We wait for the door to click shut and we burst out laughing.

"Why the hell did you tell them I was your boyfriend?"

She's trying to stifle her laughter because I can tell it hurts.

"Because I'm smart. I figured you would show up with something stupid or gross."

"Ding ding!"

"So I decided that it would probably be at least *mildly* acceptable if we were a couple."

I don't know what to say.

Tick. Tick. Tick.

She tries to break the sudden awkwardness by asking about my father.

I shift my eyes to the floor.

Breath. Throat clear. Breath.

"He's dead."

Her face drops.

"What?! Oh my God ..."

I stay silent so she can process the news.

"... Ohmygod. You were just with him, right?"

I lower my head further and she puts her hands on mine.

Tick tick tick.

I love the way her pulse feels against my fingers.

I look up, stare into her oily eyes in silence. She speaks.

"I'm speechless, Glenn."

Tick tick tick.

"Don't be. He's not really dead. I was just trying to cheer you up."

"What the *fuck*?"

"Sorry. Was that *wrong*?"

"Oh my God, Glenn."

"I just wanted you to feel better knowing someone had it worse than you."

She laughs hard.

"That is seriously the most fucked up thing anyone has ever said to me."

"I'm sorry."

She laughs, coughs.

"*The* most fucked up."

She asks if she can confess something to me.

Shit.

My heart speeds up and I shift my body to brace myself.

Snow from a fucking tree.

I don't have the strength for any more blindsides.

The gauntness of her face is highlighting her seriousness.

"You have to promise me you won't freak out."

I already know, Shelly. I love you and you love me.

"I won't. I promise."

I'll miss you so much, too.

"I don't really have cancer."

"What?"

Holy. Shit.

I laugh hard.

"Motherfucker! If I wasn't married and terminal, and you weren't in the ICU and, like, *actively* walking toward the light …"

I wipe the tears from her cheeks with the bottom of my palm and we stare into each other's eyes.

Tick. Tick.

"Shelly. Please don't be scared."

A slow smile comes to her face that has nothing to do with joy and she puts her hand on mine and looks right through me.

"I'm not scared, Glenn."

I know she is telling the truth. She's not scared. I kiss her forehead and I stand up and the giant dong rolls off the bed and onto the floor.

She tells me to leave it there and I do.

my apartment, an hour later

I'm back home, my real home with my real wife and my real son.
I open the door and I slip off my shoes.
Jen is asleep on the couch and Danny is flat against her chest and his
mouth is puckering as his body is riding the tide of her breath.
I turn the lights off and I grab a blanket from the closet and I cover
Jen's legs.
I ease myself into the armchair and I close my eyes and I exhale in a way
that feels bigger than an army of ghosts. I draw in a breath, hold it in
my lungs for as long as I can, tilt my head back, let it out and watch it
dissolve into the ceiling. I want to wake them both up and beg them to
hold me, beg them to stop the earth from swallowing me, beg them to
save me from the cancer in my blood and the even bigger cancer in my
head. Instead, I tell myself to leave it there and I do.

doctor's office, the next day

Everything in Jay's office is bronze today. The chairs the desk the walls the diplomas. All bronzed and gilded. I'm here to get some answers to my sporadic blood urine even though I know they're answers he probably can't give me. So many minor catastrophes happen during cancer treatment that leave doctors scratching their heads that I've resigned myself to being half-sure about everything. The same way I've resigned myself to the bigger catastrophes, the ones that draw invisible blood and leave invisible scars.
I watch the sun distend and disappear as I wait for Jay to finish with his other patients.
Orange.
Waiting.
Red.
Waiting.
Purple.
Waiting.
Gray.
Waiting.
Black.
Black? Shit. It's already nighttime.
I walk across the room, flip the lights on, watch the fluorescent tubes on the ceiling flicker to life like they weren't expecting to work today.
Where the hell is he?
I open the door, poke my head into the hallway. The only light in the office is a small green desk lamp on the corner of the receptionist's desk.

I call out.

Nothing.

"Jay?"

Nothing.

I walk to the empty waiting room and I take out my phone and call him.

Voicemail.

I make my way down the hallway, open every door.

Empty. Empty. Empty.

Are you kidding me?

I go back to the waiting room, call Jay again.

Voicemail.

Suddenly my body feels heavy, stilted, like I just hit the metal step at the end of a moving walkway.

Am I dead? Is this a fucking joke?

I hang up and I call my dad.

"Hey Stuie. You okay?"

"I don't know. How do I sound?"

"Like my second favorite son."

Definitely alive.

"I mean it, Dad. I don't know how I'm doing. I'm at Jay's office and I was waiting for him to go over the results of my new scans and he never came in to get me."

"What? Really? Did you talk to his nurse?"

"I came out of the office and everyone was gone."

"*Everyone* everyone?"

"Yeah."

"I assume you tried calling—?"

A beep cuts off his last word.

Jay.

"Hold on a sec, Pop. He's calling me on the other line."

I hang up, pick up.

Jay's words are metallic, flat, steady. An AM radio at the bottom of a full bathtub.

My words are even flatter.

"... please tell her dad I'm sorry."

Shelly is dead.

Shelly is dead and I am not and this sudden guilt feels like a whole different kind of death.

I close the phone and I walk across the room and I sit in her chair and I put my head in my hands and let everything fall through me. The tears the rage the loneliness the fear the numbness. I don't know if what I feel in this moment is the surrender of drowning or the breath before the dive, but right now the two feel identical.

I walk out of the building and I weave my way into the river of commuters flowing downtown and I breathe and I walk and I force myself to go as far as I can for as long as I can. I don't know how I'll make it out of this forest or even if I ever will. Nurses, doctors, friends, family, co-workers, total strangers. They all keep saying how *courageous* I am to wake up every day and push through the misery of the inevitable, how *courageous* it is for me to keep going even though I'm so scared and unsure of what lies around the next corner.

I breathe and I force myself to go as far as I can for as long as I can.

I think maybe courage is often just a profound lack of options.

downtown manhattan, minutes or hours later

I don't know how long I've been walking but I know I must've made some turns along the way because I haven't walked into the Hudson River yet. The mammoth glass evergreens that line the streets are muscular, defiant, perfectly vertical. The tallest of them, indestructible twins that lord over the rest of the island. I want to be as permanent as those towers.

My face is stripped raw from tears and wind and snot. I keep looking up to follow the handful of clouds that seem hell-bent on hiding my view of the moon, the only light in tonight's moldy black sky. I pass a bodega and I bump into a guy who looks like he's being paid to guard the fresh flowers. He yells something at my back and I don't know what the hell he's saying and I don't care. He could knock me out with a tire iron and crush my teeth into chalk dust and somehow it would feel fitting with the rest of this.

My phone starts to buzz.

My heart flutters when I see Shelly's name on the screen.

"Glenn? Eric. Shelly's father."

My throat tightens.

"I'm so sorry to hear about Shelly."

His voice is brittle, defeated. A rubber band left out the sun.

"Thank you, Glenn."

I scramble to fill the silence under his tears by offering to come over and keep him company.

Go home, Glenn.

Go home and be with your own *child and your* real *wife.*

"That's really kind of you, Glenn but I'd prefer to be alone right now."

"Of course. Well, I'm here for whenever you come up for air, even if that's a year from now."

"Shelly told us about *your* health and I just wanted to tell you that I'm here for you however you need me."

His kindness floors me. I stop and I lean my back against a plywood wall and I slide down to the sidewalk and I speak through a bubble of mucus.

"Thank you …"

I can't breathe.

"I mean it, Glenn."

My voice stutters as my lungs struggle for air.

"I know, you, do."

He is silent for several seconds, then forces a pained laugh to get his composure.

"Glenn. I'm calling mostly to thank you for what you gave Shelly when you were here."

My skin goes cold.

Oh my God.

"I don't know what you said to her but her whole energy changed when you left. She was lighter. Calmer. She was … *happy?* … for lack of a better word."

I let out a long exhale as he continues.

"The last thing she said was *I'm not scared.*"

"I really thought you were gonna say something about the dong."

Oh my God.

"I'm sorry, what?"

Throw your fucking phone into the street.

"Nothing. I don't think I'm making much sense right now."

Kill yourself, Glenn.

Eric says *thank you again* and adds *for what it's worth* and I tell him it's worth more than he knows.

I hear Shelly telling me to leave it there and I do.

I walk and I breathe and I force myself to go as far as I can for as long as I can.

I've gone as long as I should.

my apartment, late evening

I shut the front door gently behind me and I slip off my sneakers and I
pad my way to the kitchen.

Home.

Jen turns and looks at me like I'm a stranger holding a machete.

What's wrong with her?

I ignore the tension and I kiss her head and I pick Danny up from the
bouncy spectator chair she's set up for him on the counter. He's having a
good time watching her cook and he gets fussy when I move him.

Jen pulls steaming pasta from the colander, sighs, speaks.

"I *just* managed to get him calmed down, Glenn."

"Sorry."

"It's fine. But good luck getting him comfortable again."

I turn Danny's face to mine, lift him into the air, make a face that always
makes him smile. It doesn't work. He fusses as Jen continues.

"So where've you been? Last I heard from you, you were stopping to see
someone at the hospital after you got off the train."

Shit. Is that possible?

"That wasn't the last time we talked, was it? When I got home from the
hospital last night you guys were sleeping."

My phone vibrates and I glance at the screen.

Dad.

I let his call go to voicemail even though I want to pick up.

Jen carries two steaming plates to the dining room table and insists I
start eating.

"We *were* sleeping. But when we woke up, you'd already left for work."

I bounce Danny on my knee and try not to wince as I eat. The tomato sauce feels like lava in my throat but I know I have to eat as much as I can as often as I can.

"Jesus, Jen. I didn't even realize that. I think I'm in some kind of weird autopilot mode."

She sits and alternates spoonfuls with Danny.

"Okay, Glenn—"

It's not okay.

"—doesn't matter. Did you get the results from your new scans yet?"

"I didn't. I was supposed to go over them with Jay but he had to bolt out of the office and he forgot about me."

"What do you mean he forgot about you?"

"That girl I visited in the hospital the other night? She died quicker than he expected her to I guess."

"Oh my god. That's horrible. Wait, *what* girl?"

"Shelly. The one I met in Jay's waiting room?"

Danny slams his hand onto his small plastic plate and sends it flying across the room.

It doesn't register.

"You never told me about a girl you met at Jay's office."

"Yes I did."

I'm defiant about something I don't remember.

She picks up her plate, walks back to the kitchen, raises her voice to reiterate that I didn't tell her about Shelly, adding *it doesn't matter* and that she's sorry I *lost my friend.*

I set my fork down, rest my cheek on Danny's head.

"Of *course* it matters. And you're not sorry she's dead. And that's okay. Either way, I'm sorry. I thought I told you."

She walks back into the room, speaks through a pained smile.

"You'd have to actually *be home* to tell me things, Glenn."

I apologize again and she ignores me.

We both know if I were genuinely sorry, I'd be making different choices about how I spend my time.

"How old was she?"

"I think he said she was twenty-five."

Jen stares out the window behind me, mumbles.

"That's way too young."

I hand Danny over to her, start to collect my dishes.

"You know what else is too young? Twenty-eight. *My* age—"

Stop stop stop.

"—your husband's age. Danny's father?"

Don't be an asshole. She's hurting.

The radiator clicks its tongue, lets out a long sigh. I want to pull her into my arms and kiss her and tell her how much I love her and how sorry I am for being so far away.

I don't do any of those things and I don't know why.

She looks up at me and grins the way she does when she's swallowing her words.

She motions for me to set my plate back down.

"Just leave it there."

She walks back into the kitchen alone.

I leave it there.

my bathroom, forty-five minutes later

I close the door, peel off my clothes, wait for the shower to get as hot as possible. The air turns to milk-fog and I sit on the edge of the tub and make slow-motion karate chops through the steam. It calms me, this tiny box in the sky surrounded by brick and glass and metal. I am warm and I am safe.

Shit. My dad's call.

I pull the phone from the front pocket of my jeans and I dial. He speaks before I even hear a ring.

"That's okay, Glenn. Don't worry about me. It's totally normal to be talking to your dying father and then take another call in the middle of it and never call him back. The man who raised you and fed you and nurtured you and protected you. The man who is rotting away in the corner of a tiny room in—"

"You done yet?"

He asks me what happened with Jay and I tell him he forgot about our appointment.

"Did you tell him off?"

"What? Why would I do that? He had more important stuff to deal with."

"You really pick some strange times to be assertive, Stuie. One minute you're punching some guy's golf umbrella and the next minute you're trying not to upset someone who left you alone in a room for two hours."

"He didn't mean to leave me there."

"You're always gonna be that Easter Basket kid."

Jay didn't mean to leave me alone.

doctor's office, the next day

I stare out the window behind Jay's desk and I watch another sun sink
down behind the skyline.
He pokes his head into the room and tells me he'll be in shortly with my
newest scans. I tell him to take his time. I don't want to see them. I hate
the power they hold over me and I have no power left to give. Even if it's
good news, it'll do nothing to calm my heart.
There is Cancer and there is No Cancer.
Everything in between is still Cancer.
I focus on the sunset, on the beauty, on the long glowing red band of sky
widening and softening. A darkroom door cut a few inches too short.
Jay walks in and puts the films against the lightbox like an auctioneer
unveiling a shitty oil painting. The glowing black and white landscape is
like a bird's eye view of a funeral. He asks me what I think.
"What do you *mean* what do I think?"
I'm always perplexed by his timing choices when it comes to showcasing
his non-clinical personality.
"You're like a kitten, Jay. Being cute is the only thing keeping you from
getting chucked out a window. Just *tell me* what they mean."
He points to the films again and tells me to take a guess.
"I'm gonna murder you so hard in the face if you don't just fucking
tell me, Jay."
He draws air circles with the back of his pen over a couple shadowed
areas on the film.
"Still two small ones here. *Buuut* no more tumors here, here … or here."
Some are gone. Some remain.

This is what a moment is and what a moment means and why moments can make a person feel lost forever if those moments never end.

I am relieved and I am angry and I am scared and I am grateful and I am totally fucking adrift. I am all of these things all at once.

I should be happy, hopeful, rolling around in the elation of all these bright new colors.

But I'm not.

All the colors are overlapping and blending together and now there is only the hideous brown color of a rainbow that's been stuffed into a can and shaken to paste.

"This is good news, Glenn."

I have no words.

All I see in those glowing shadows and empty spaces is more minutes, hours, days, weeks. I am getting better as my father is getting worse and the guilt I feel right now feels like yet another death. The sun is gone and the darkroom light is off and the films are developed.

waiting room, twenty minutes later

Everything is dark and eerily quiet as I wait for Jay to finish closing shop. I sit and I count the clicking of light switches and the slow hiss-clunking of exam room doors.

Nine lights, six doors.

I raise my voice to remind him that my train to Boston leaves in a couple of hours.

He suggests we get something to eat, tells me "we need to talk."

Fun.

I try not to look at Shelly's row of chairs against the wall in the reception area on our way out.

"Did you want to check and make sure you didn't leave any patients in there, JJ?"

He says nothing as he locks the door. I push the elevator button and I continue as if he's actually been participating in the conversation.

"Did I ever tell you what my dad says about why I'm annoying like this?"

We get on, assume the elevator position. He's silent as I speak to the closing doors.

"No? Well, my grandma used to tell him that just because you shed light on a situation, it doesn't *necessarily* mean you take a situation lightly …"

He nods a reluctant yes.

"… and there's *no* part of me that takes any of this lightly, JJ. I just know that I'll drown if I don't say these stupid things to buoy myself."

He turns and looks at me like I've insulted his intelligence.

"Glenn. Just consider the fact that you're not the only scared one, okay? The people who love you are also doing their best not to drown."

I reach out and I pull him toward me and I kiss his head and I stop myself from sharing the only thought in my head: *I'm tired of making sure everyone else is okay with me dying.*

"Thank you, JJ. I really do fucking love you."

We get to the lobby, push through the revolving doors, charge headfirst into the night air. Cigarette smoke, hot dogs, car exhaust, piss, perfume, burnt chestnuts, garbage, fresh horse shit. This city is its own constant assault. As we walk, he dodges an umbrella and points to a diner on the corner glowing every color of neon imaginable. We walk in and we weave our way through the crowd and we settle into a booth next to the window. Jay runs his fingers through his hair as he speaks.

"Okay, Glenn. A couple things ..."

Fuck. He's all business.

"I looked at all your dad's scans and I had a chat with his doctor. And you're right. The guy's a huge prick—"

Thank you.

"—but unfortunately, the prick is right."

"Meaning?"

A balding, hairy-armed man in a white button-down and stained white apron walks over and sets two glasses of water onto the edge of our table. His thumb is on the outside of the glass and three of his fingers are on the inside.

That's fun.

"Drink your knuckle water, Jay."

He takes a sip, ignores my comment.

"Meaning it doesn't look good, G."

My skin tightens and washes cold.

"JJ, did you see the way he was holding the water glasses? He had each one of his hairy fucking fingers right in—"

"Glenn! Stop."

"Sorry. I'm listening."

"Did you hear what I said?"

"You said it *doesn't look good,* but why's it suddenly different now?"

"His treatment isn't working. *At all.* So now I'm worried about time."

The waiter walks back over and stands in silence, pen poised over his order pad like a threat. I open my menu and Jay orders a salad and I order a tuna fish sandwich because it's the first thing I see.

"You hate tuna fish, G."

"I know but that guy scares me."

"Anyway, it's likely gonna be soon and it's likely gonna be quick."

Soon. Quick.

His words hang in the air.

Soon. Quick.

My chest is filling with mud.

Soon. Quick.

A sudden undulating nausea moves right through me. A relentless churning, a ball of razor wire in a cement mixer. I stare out the window and I watch a wild-eyed homeless man unzip his fly and piss all over the only tree on the block.

my father's bedroom, next day

The window above his bed is steaming up around the edges as the wind slams the falling snow against the house. His belly is more distended than it's ever been and I can't stop staring at it while he sleeps. I know Jay said *soon* but I'm not ready.

Fuck this.

I ease myself onto the bed and I slip my arm under his and I decide I'll just refuse to let go.

Thirty-six minutes.

Thirty-seven.

I position my face less than an inch from his and I watch his eyeballs dart back and forth like he's following a high-speed tennis match behind his lids.

I let out a soft lecherous moan and the tennis match stops and he opens his eyes and mumbles a plea to let him sleep.

I moan again and I tell him he's pretty.

He cracks a slow smile.

"There's something *so* wrong with you, Stuie."

"That's why I'm waking you up, Dad. You're a shrink. Fix me before we die."

"You don't need fixing. At least not in the ways you think you do."

I laugh.

"But you're the one who tells me I'm broken *all the time*, Pop."

He's suddenly activated, lucid, energized.

There he is.

He uses his elbows to push himself up against the headboard, his pregnant body now L-shaped and very much awake.

"I'm just busting your balls, Stuie. You're broken, but you're the good kinda broken."

"Oh. *Good* broken! That makes me feel better. Is that like a *sexy* burn victim?"

"C'mon, Glenn. You're italic."

"You've said that to me before and I still have no fucking idea what it means."

"*Italic?* Just like it sounds. You stand out."

"Still struggling to find the positive here, Pop."

"Jesus. Italic is a *good thing*, Stuie. In my opinion—which we can all agree is really the only opinion that matters—the only people worth knowing are the ones who were forged in pain some way or another. They're the interesting ones. The *italic* ones. Are you following me or should I bust out the crayons?"

"I was joking. I don't need you to fix me, Pop. I just woke you up to be a dick."

I woke you up because I'm losing you.

He sighs, closes his eyes.

"You don't need to be fixed, Stuie."

I do.

Andrea opens the bedroom door and whispers.

"Sorry to interrupt, guys."

I hear Julia in the distance still singing along to her stereo.

"You're not interrupting at all, Dre. I assume you're trying to get a break from that fucking song?"

My dad yells.

"Hey, watch the language, Stu. And leave your sister alone."

"C'mon, Dad. That Barbie song is a violation of the goddamn Geneva Convention."

He's pissed.

I guess eleven years old is too young to hear bad words.

Andrea laughs, tells us she's taking Julia with her to run some errands, tells us she won't hate us if the Barbie CD somehow disappears while they're out.

I love her.

My dad lets out a huge sigh as she closes the door.

"Sorry, Pop. I was just trying to lighten the room a little."

"It's not your job to make everything less heavy, Glenn …"

I'd be fucking horizontal if I didn't.

"Now make yourself useful and put on another *Studs*."

I'm fine with italic.

I get up, slip a cassette into the VCR, hand him the remote, flop backwards onto the bed and watch the dust fall over us like dying fireworks.

my father's bedroom, that night

The room is dark, almost black. I find the nightstand, turn on the
lamp, watch it slowly fill the room with warm yellow light. The color
accentuates all my dad's new dents and divots and lumps.

This is a new shape I don't recognize. The thing underneath that
comforter is not my father. It's an art department prop, a retired exhibit
from Area 51, a flea market remnant no one wants.

I curl myself into his side and wrap my arm over his unborn child as
he breathes.

He opens his eyes.

"Stuie ..."

He adjusts his body and makes a sad attempt to bunch up his pillows.

I avoid his eyes and the mound of nonexistent infant inside his belly.

I sit up and I wait for the rest of his words.

"What, Dad?"

"*What* what?"

"You said *Stuie* but then you didn't finish."

His eyes search the corner of the ceiling.

"I forgot."

I hate every one of these new hiccups in time.

"Oh yeah, I remember ... What happened with your scans?"

I can't decide if telling him I got good news will buoy him or send a
signal to his brain to stop fighting now that his only prayer is closer to
being answered.

"I still have chemo next week so I'm not sure things are getting better."

"What did Jay say?"

"He said some of the tumors are gone."

"Really? So your take-away from that is you're *not sure* things are getting better?"

I have a knack for finding the only grain of salt in an ocean of sugar.

"I'm just trying not to get my hopes up, Pop."

His eyes widen and his body is suddenly electric and sober again. There's something primal in these shifts in lucidity. Almost like the thinning of time is activating some paternal instinct.

"I get that, Stuie. But you need to shift the way that brain of yours works. You're always walking around with this sad little storm cloud over your head. You've been that way ever since you were little."

I can give you an exact date.

"I was depressed, Pop."

"You were *sad*, not depressed. Big difference."

"I really don't need the psych seminar."

"Trust me, Stuie. You do. This is important to get through that thick melon of yours: being sad isn't static. The same way being happy isn't static. Being sad is wet cement. And wet cement falls off as long as you're in motion."

"Now you're making me look forward to death."

He ignores me and continues.

"Depression's a different beast. Depression is letting that cement dry. And it *will* dry and it *will* harden if you let it. And then you could fall into the shallowest stream and still drown. That make sense?"

I can tell there's more he wants to say by the way his milky eyes search the ceiling, as if the answers are written in the plaster, hidden under layers of paint.

"It really comes down to this …"

He stops, tries to find his footing.

"Depression is really just your brain's inability to create a future for itself."

His eyes brighten with relief that he was able to get his whole thought out intact.

"And you can only create that future if the cement stays wet. It's really fucking important that you understand that, Stuie."

"I do, Pop."

I half-understand but it doesn't matter because the rest of his sermon is already written.

"People will offer up bullshit platitudes like '*time heals all*' and '*tomorrow will be better*' as if a fortune cookie sentiment is all your brain needs to imagine a future. It's well-intentioned but—"

I stand and I walk over to a stack of VHS tapes on the windowsill and I tell him *keep talking*, tell him *I'm listening*.

I grab one labeled *First MBW* and I flip it around in my hands as he finishes his thought.

"—I think it's probably more honest to say this: tomorrow may not be *better* but it will be *different*. And different is the only path to better."

I hold up the cassette and I ask him what the label means and he squints until he can read the spine. He smiles.

"MBW! That was our first Male Bonding Weekend."

"The one in San Francisco?"

"Yup. That was *fun*, wasn't it?"

Fun. There's that word again.

"Did you hear what I said, Stu?"

"Yes!"

He extends his upturned hand as a way of cueing me to repeat what I just heard.

I roll my eyes, speak in monotone.

"Tomorrow may not be better, but it will be different."

"Annnd...?"

"And different is the only path to better."

"Good boy. Now let's watch that goddamn video."

We laugh.

I slip the tape into the VCR and I climb back into bed and watch as the TV flickers through clips of Nate and me trudging through Golden Gate Park. Judging from my feathered hair and swollen boy boobs, I would guess I was probably eleven years old at the time. This was the first of many *male-bonding weekends* my father organized after he and my mother divorced. Each *MBW* wound up being a mix of boredom, yelling, and shitty hotel meals. He declared all of them a success nonetheless.

"Look at the sheer joy on our faces, Pop."

He sighs at my sarcasm and clicks his tongue.

"*Of course* you guys were miserable. Jews weren't meant to be outdoors."

This is fun.

"Remember our first night at the hotel, Pop?"

"Not really. Remind me."

Nate is in the shower and I'm on a foldout cot at the foot of my dad's double bed. The hotel air is thick with decades-old nicotine and sweat and we're in hour four of our TV-watching marathon. My blood's starting to itch the way it always does when it feels like time is thinning.

"Hey Dad."

His eyes stay glued to the illuminated nothingness.

"What?"

"Nate's been in the shower for almost forty-five minutes."

He clears his throat and yells.

"Nate! Stop masturbating!"

Silence.

What the hell?

An Energizer commercial buzzes away behind me.

"You happy now, Glenn?"

"I guess?"

I stand and I walk over to Nate's bed, strip off the linens, lift up the mattress and prop it against the wall.

My dad speaks without taking his eyes off the TV.

"What the hell are you doing, Stuie?"

"I'm putting Nate's bed in the hallway."

His eyes turn to meet mine and they soften in a way that says *I love this but I can't condone this.* He picks up the remote, turns off the TV, pulls the blanket up just under his nose and mumbles *this should be interesting* through a smile I can't see.

> "You were such an idiot, Stuie."
>
> "You ever wonder why I was always acting out?"
>
> He laughs dismissively, pauses the VCR, speaks.
>
> "You went from being such a quiet kid to suddenly wanting to mess with everyone's head. Don't get me wrong, I know that's a 'comedian's' job.' It's just that you just seemed to hone that skill so young."
>
> "Like what age, you think, Pop? 'Cause I think I have some idea when it started."
>
> *Leave him alone.*
>
> He lets out a long heavy sigh and shakes his head. He's not in the mood to be provoked.
>
> I swallow the sting, go back to reminiscing, go back to burying.

I prop open the door and I drag the mattress across the dark maroon carpet and into the hallway. I walk back into the room and I grab the box spring and steel frame and I wrestle them through the threshold until only the headboard remains, bolted to the wall. A nicely dressed couple at the end of the hall leaves their room and stares at my mess and I wave because I don't know what else to do. I go back into the room and I turn off the lights and I feel my way back to my cot as my father titters away under the blanket.

Black.

Silence.

The squeak of the rusty tub faucet.

Shower curtain screech.

Silence.

The bathroom door opens and the steam bursts out like a low-budget UFO landing. Nate walks out, nothing but bushy wet hair and tight white underpants. He turns off the bathroom light and he feels his way to a table near the door.

My father has buried his head under all his pillows.

My eyes have adapted to the dark so I can see what Nate can't.

I am delighted.

He feels the edge of my father's bed with both hands and does the *my-bed-must-be-a-few-inches-from-here* math and falls back onto the invisible mattress. The carpet-on-concrete thud shakes the room.

"What the fuck?!"

My eyes are watering and my dad's bed is vibrating with silent laughter and I don't think either of us can believe he hasn't yet figured out that his bed is missing.

He crawls around on the floor, waving blindly in front of him like a cartoon bookworm searching for their glasses.

He finds the nightstand, feels his way up the lamp, pushes its bronze belly button and the room fills with soft yellow light.

"What the *fuck* did you assholes do!"

My dad wheeze-laughs until he coughs.

Nate storms over to my cot, unleashes a thunderstorm of punches onto my pillow-covered head, marches over to the door, sees his bed set up in the hallway and steps out. The door slams shut behind him.

Locked.

We laugh and we laugh and we laugh and then for some reason my father attempts to discipline me through the laughs.

"That was *not* cool, Stuie."

Laughcoughwheeze.

His weak attempt at high-roading makes me laugh even harder until
I start to pee. Nate slams his fists against the door over and over as I
continue to empty my bladder onto the cot.

Slam.

Pee.

Slam.

Pee.

Suddenly, my dad yells at me like he's just arrived on the scene.

"Open the door for him, Stuie. C'mon!"

I stand and I walk to the door in my soaked pajamas and Nate tackles me
to the ground and punches me for almost ten seconds before he realizes
his own underpants are now soaked.

"What the hell is *this*?!"

The room goes quiet.

"I peed."

Nate slaps me on the forehead with his palm as he stands.

"You pissed the bed while you were *awake*?"

"Yes?"

"What the fuck is *wrong* with you?"

"I don't know."

My dad is suddenly furious with this bizarre tableau splayed out in front
of him.

He lets out a big sigh, walks to the hotel fridge, grabs a Fresca, takes a sip
and shakes his head as if he can't believe what he's just walked in on.

"You guys are pathetic."

Males bonded.

My father's face is sweaty and gray as I finish the story and I can tell from
his disoriented stare that he must have stopped listening at some point.

"You okay, Pop?"

My heart starts flailing like a botched yoyo toss.

"Can I get you something, Dad?"

He waves me away without lifting his arm off the bed.

"I'm okay, I'm okay."

"You sure, Pop?"

I scoot up next to him and I put my hand on the back of his head and I
feel the two tall tendons in the back of his neck that resemble the number
eleven as they struggle to keep his head upright. I've spent enough time
with people during the final weeks of their lives through Best Medicine

to recognize some of the darkest, unmistakable signs of death. The *elevens* are one of those signs. I don't want to know these signs. I don't want to know a single fucking thing about how death looks.

He leans his face into my open palm and he closes his eyes and he breathes slowly through the puckered O shape of his paper lips.

I kiss his hair as he draws a long breath.

He tells me he's okay.

"I'm okay until I'm not."

my father's bedroom, next morning

The sun is here again, bleaching all the color from the room like a tv
show flashback. I walk to the bathroom and I pee sitting down and I look
at my phone and I see that Jay called at some point in the middle of the
night. I open my phone and call him back.
"Everything okay, JJ?"
"You need to get your dad to the ER."
A sudden stop in my throat, an invisible softball. My voice thins to get
around it.
"Whassgoing on, J?"
"The stomach distension. I just got into a fight with your dad's doc. To
me, it's clearly a bowel obstruction and I'm worried about it going septic."
"Wait, what? Why doesn't his doctor doesn't agree?"
"He thinks it can wait until he sees your dad in a couple days. I don't
think it can."
"Fuckfuck. Okay, JJ. I'm on it. Thank y—"
Click.
I walk downstairs and I tell Andrea and she tells me she already knows,
tells me she *just found out.* Apparently, my father's doctor just called
her. A painfully transparent attempt to cover his own ass in case Jay's
assessment is right.
We head upstairs, wake my father, get him dressed, get him into the car,
give him his steel mixing bowl in case he needs to puke on the way there
and do our best impression of nonchalance as we drive.
Music plays.

None of us are able to make small talk.

I tap out the rhythm on the dashboard, pretending it's not the rhythm of my heart trying to find its way out of my chest.

hospital parking garage, eighty-eight minutes later

We pass under the white tongue of the parking garage gate, usher him through the sliding glass hospital mouth, ease him into the belly of the wheelchair, push him over to a smiling male nurse shaped like a fire hydrant.

My dad's voice is high, arced, confused. A child being dropped off at summer camp for a month.

"Are you leaving me?"

"We'll be in the waiting room, Pop."

The nurse tells us to have a seat wherever we'd like and assures us he'll take good care of him.

His words calm me.

Thank you, fire hydrant. Thank you.

Andrea and I sit and we wait and we talk and we wait and we pace and we eat and we wait and we pace and we sit and we wait.

Over and over again for hours.

I feel like I'm watching all of this from above, like all these passing hours are just some shitty time-lapse security footage.

We wait and we talk and we wait and we pace and we eat and we wait and we pace and we talk and we sit and we wait.

Then:

The Man In the White Cape arrives to give us good news.

I wish I had even an ounce of my dad's doctor's unearned self-confidence.

"Just a bowel obstruction. Should be fairly simple surgery. The rest of the scan looked totally normal."

"Really? The rest looked *normal?*"

I don't buy it. I want to exhale but I know I can't.

Something's off and I know it. I know it the way the blind and deaf must know when they aren't alone in a room. I know what we're hearing and seeing doesn't line up with what we're both feeling right now.

The Man In the White Cape tells us to have a seat, tells us everything is okay, tells us everything is normal, tells us someone will come and get us in a few hours when my father is ready for visitors, tells us *absolutely no visitors until then.*

The Man In the White Cape is the sun in our endless blue sky.

He's the *crystal-clear streams.*

He's the *rolling wildflower fields.*

He's the big beautiful lie.

Nothing is *normal.* Nothing is as it was or what I was told it would be.

Fuck.

Suddenly my body feels fluid, viscous, unbound.

Run. Runrunrun.

Go, Glenn.

I get that weird belly tickle I used to get long ago, that catching-the-lip-of-the-table-right-before-the-chair-tips-too-far-back-and-crashes-to-the-ground feeling.

The Man In the White Cape told us to wait.

Fuck him.

The Man In the White Cape told us to wait.

He is the sun in our clear blue sky, and that sun is a big fucking lie.

It's been lying to me my whole life.

It's time to go.

It's time to go.

Now.

hospital basement level, minutes later

Andrea and I wander the recesses of the unit until we are spit out into a large room seemingly subdivided by survival odds. The air is milky and dense and heavy in a way I assume it must be all the time in here, a fog of loss that hovers above the unlucky ones waiting to walk the plank.
We push aside the curtain dividers one by one.
Dad?
No.
Dad?
Nope.
Dad?
No.
There he is.
Exhale.
We close the curtain behind us and we walk to either side of his bed and we each take one of his hands.
Oh my God.
They feel like translucent bat wings, cold and thin and taut.
"We're here, Pop."
Andrea runs her fingers through his soft curls and mumbles *oh honey* over and over as she shoulder-wipes a steady ellipsis of tears from her cheek.
"You're gonna be fine, Pop. I promise."
I bring my face right up to his and I watch his eyes float over me as if they're studying the shapes of my lies.
They're oily, dilated, disoriented. A clubbed fish left flailing on the dock.

I get close enough to see the reflection of my own face. It looks the way I feel inside: convex, bent, pretzeled. My forehead is puckered and my nose is wide and the half-moon skin below my eyes is the color of smoke. I run my fingers through his hair and I kiss his forehead and I put my lips to his ear and I tell him I'm jealous of his upcoming bowel surgery.

"Whatever you do, do *not* have fun."

A smile creeps from his cracked lips.

"*There* you are, Pop."

I let go of his hand and I kiss him until his hair is damp and I tell him he's in good hands, tell him we'll see him tomorrow, *we'll see you tomorrow, Pop.*

Andrea and I walk out to the car in silence and we drive home under a purpleblue sky the color of a cartoon breath held too long.

I hope I wasn't lying when I told him we would see him tomorrow.

Fifty-seven is too young to be left alone.

I hope I wasn't lying.

I don't want to be his sun.

andrea's house, two hours later

I kiss Andrea goodnight and I ask her if I can stay in their bed tonight
and she says *of course of course*, get some sleep, *everything will be okay*.
The bedside lamp is on and the room is the color of hay and I'm alone on
his bed and I'm sifting through the stack of magazines on his nightstand
as *Studs* plays on the muted television.
One of the covers shows a forest of pine trees leading up to the edge of an
anonymous coastline, paralyzed and angled and fleeing a storm just out
of frame.
There's a lone tree that's closer to the sea than the others and it's almost
horizontal. I can see the violence of the wind even though it's just a
single snapshot.
I *know* that fucking tree at the foot of the ocean and I know that angle
and I know those brittle fists.
I bury my face in his pillow and I inhale him. Antiseptic musky primal.
I hold him inside my lungs for as long as I can before rolling back over
and letting him go.
I sit and I watch the hay turn to fire and the fire turn to charcoal and
the charcoal turn to iron and I close my eyes and I picture him in the
distance at the far end of the road that splits right through the heart of
camp, heat rising from the dirt, his body wavering like an old detuned
tv set.
No more sleeps. It's over.
I am here. Brittle fists up and ready.

still day 24

The trees on both sides of the road leading down to the center of camp
are dark and tall and perfect.
Even though I'm small, I feel taller than I was when I got here.
It's not a good kind of tall.
It's an old kind of tall that feels like I got stretched out.
Like something happened to my body without me saying it was okay.
Two boys from the older cabins come up behind me with huge duffel
bags strapped to their backs and one of them yells at me as they pass.
"Pick up your trunk, fag! You're makin' too much dust!"
"Go suck a horse dick."
I feel tough enough for those words now.
"Ooh. Big words for a little man."
"Sit on it!"
Good job, Glenn.
I get to the top of the hill and I stop in the middle of the fog to catch my
breath. I see a big group of grown-ups standing around the flagpole in
the distance and I want to drop my trunk and run as fast as I can down
the hill and into the crowd and find my mom and my dad and wrap my
arms around them and never let them go.
"Stuie!"
Dad?
My father's voice feels like one of those warm crinkly silver blankets they
wrap around marathon runners after they cross the finish line. I feel like
one of those runners. Like I'm one of those people strangers take care of.

I squint and I wave even though I can't see him.

"Dad?"

I see his hands waving back and forth like one of those guys with the flashlights at the airport, like he's waving me in.

My skin feels softer with every step closer to his voice.

"Dad?"

My bones feel softer too.

"Dad?"

I feel the tears coming even though I know they won't.

"Stuie!"

His face, his smile. His big green eyes look like those hot springs in the travel magazines that people sit in even though they're surrounded by snow.

I let go of the trunk handle and run over to him as fast as I can and I wrap my arms around his legs and I squeeze as hard as my arms will let me.

I want to live in this moment forever.

I have learned what a moment is and what a moment means and why moments can make a person happy forever if those moments never end.

"That's enough, Stu."

His voice sounds colder than it used to and I don't like it.

He starts to pry my hug loose.

What's he doing?

I squeeze harder.

He pries harder.

"Glenn. Enough! What's wrong with you?"

I let go and I look up into his eyes and they don't feel like those green hot springs anymore.

They feel like the snow that surrounds them.

I guess it's weak to love someone so much and I don't want to be weak.

All of these sleeps with the lions taught me that much.

From now on, I'll just be the snow.

my father's bed, seven hours later

Andrea wakes me and tells me it's time, *it's time*, tells me we have to go
back to the hospital. The pregnant man is ready to give birth.
I call Jen as we drive.
"Everything okay, Glenn?"
"It's time."
The same words she used when she called to tell me Danny was on his
way into the world.
I count the silent seconds between us.
Sixty-one Sixty-two Sixty-three Sixty-four.
"I love you."
Silence.
Everything between *I love you* and arriving at the ICU is black.
I'm not even sure which one of us said those three words.
Black.
Black.
Black.
We're here and it's time.

intensive care unit, sixty-four minutes later

The sunlight pours in through the window and turns the room to a blown-out flashcube, everything frozen white and charred at the edges.
I was right.
The surgery *wasn't* simple and the scans *were* a lie and the considered-one-of-the-best-oncologists *is* sorry.
But it doesn't matter now.
It's time.
Andrea stands at the foot of the bed and holds his feet in her hands.
Her chest is heaving and she can no longer control her sobbing.
I walk over to my dad's head, run my trembling thumb across his forehead, study his face. His lips are dry and bloody and a thick brown stomach syrup pools in his mouth and occasionally drips down his cheek.
I grab a tissue from the shelf above his head and I wipe his face and the corners of his mouth.
As I dab the liquid away, I feel a break in time that I haven't felt since that night in the forest when day turned to night, when the sun disappeared with a blink, when my time found its first hyphen.
I hold my dad's head in my hands.
I blink.
The room goes silent.
I blink.
The electric green numbers on the screen above his head start to plummet and the lights flash and the sirens ring out and the frantic beep of the alarm is suddenly underwater.

I put my head against his and I whisper through a clear film of saltwater.
"It's okay to let go. It's okay to let go, Pop."
I feel my lips stuck to his forehead from mucus and tears.
I breathe in.
He breathes out.
I breathe in.
He breathes out.
The numbers blur and the light from the window dips to gray from a
passing cloud and suddenly I am six years old again.

I am six years old and standing with my dad outside the chain-link fence
that surrounds the tarmac of the West Palm Beach airport. There are so
many people here and most of them are crying. Some of them are waving
to the people on the plane and my dad is waving to the people on the
plane and since he's my dad I wave to them too.
I see a tiny hand in the row of windows running down the length of the
plane. I imagine the hand in the window is my mom's and that she wants
me to run out there and pull her out of her seat and bring her back to us.
I don't want her to go.
The plane rolls past the fence and my dad picks me up and shields me
from the metallic wind blowing from its giant engines. There's saltwater
in the air and there's saltwater streaming down his face. He kisses my
hair and he squeezes me against his chest as the plane speeds down the
runway and into the air. We watch as it gets smaller and smaller until it's
just another bird in the Florida sky and then we watch it disappear into
the clouds.
All the people around us walk away and get back into their cars and I
think about how sad all those people must be now that everyone they
love has gone away.
My dad sees me crying.
"It's okay, Stuie—"
His light brown curls sway in the breeze and the vibration from his voice
feels big and safe.
"—imagine how all those *other* people feel."
"What other people?"
"The people waiting at the *other* airport for that exact same plane to land.
In a couple hours, they'll get to wave hello instead of goodbye."
I stare up into his eyes and I say nothing.
"Does that make sense?"

I nod *yes* even though it doesn't.

He smiles because he knows I'm lying.

I slip my hand into his and we walk to the car as he tries to explain again. "Okay. Try to imagine this, Stuie …"

He buckles me into my seat, gets behind the wheel, starts the car, turns to look at me.

"By the time we get back to Grandma's house, that plane that Mom is on right now will poke through the clouds *again*. And instead of getting smaller like it did when we watched it fly away, it'll get bigger and bigger and bigger for all the people waiting outside the fence at the airport in New York. And then *those* people will get to hug them just like we just did when they left. They'll get to wave hello instead of goodbye."

I mostly understand what he means but it doesn't matter because he's in the car with me and he's here and here is all I want and here is all I need.

The lights flash and the sirens ring out and the frantic beep of the heart monitor alarm blares sharper, louder.

I cry and I cry and I cry. I can't breathe.

I cry and I can't breathe.

Goodbye, Dad.

Crying gasping crying.

The beep goes steady, then silent.

The nurse has muted the robot.

I can't breathe, Andrea can't breathe.

Goodbye, Dad.

I want to be on the other side of this.

Goodbye, Dad.

I want to be on the other side of those clouds.

I want to wave hello but goodbye is all I have.

my father's car, later

I drive us home and I drop Andrea off at the end of the driveway and I
tell her that I'm going to drive around alone for a while.
I drive and I drive and I drive and the smell of my dad is narcotic and it's
everywhere. I hold it in my lungs for as long as I can, breathe out, step
harder on the accelerator and try to ignore the speed of trees flying by
my window. His steel mixing bowl on the empty seat is shaking to the
rhythm of the snow-broken asphalt.
"Look at this, Pop."
I point to the blur that frames our windshield.
"Nothing can be this perfect."
Rows and rows of trees, tall and green and copy-pasted all the way to the
horizon, a corduroy road indifferent to all of this.
It doesn't care how fast I'm driving and it doesn't care why I'm crying
and it doesn't care that his seat is empty and it doesn't care that now only
frost clings to the air where he just was or that the narcotic is evaporating
with each passing mile.
My hands grip the wheel and a disconnection overtakes me as if I'm
watching the car from above, a cliché that's suddenly not a cliché, the
power lines crisscross in perfect unison playing cat's cradle on either side
of the road. The world is so much fucking simpler when it's blurry.

my apartment, three days later

As of two hours and nine minutes ago, my father and I are now officially on opposite sides of the ground.

I lie on my bed and I stare at the ceiling, still in my black suit and mud-caked dress shoes. The tiny waves of Danny's breath and the smell of his sweet milkskin aren't calming me tonight the way they have every other night. My heart is different now. It's scattered and dense and mangled and electric. A ball of tin foil in a microwave.

I know this can't sustain if I'm going to see my son grow up and Jay called me at the funeral this afternoon to tell me I just might. He exhaled a long slow breath and he said that magical word through the phone. *Remission*. That magical word on the day I buried my father. *Remission*. That magical word on the day God answered one atheist's only prayer. *Remission*. I *might* get to see my son grow up.

I can hear my father's confused voice from that afternoon we circled the neighborhood in his car.

"That was my answer, Stuie: *might*."

Might. Unbreakable strength or endless unknowns.

He wasn't confused.

memorial service, two weeks later

The sky above my father's backyard is beautiful today. Never-ending and cloudless, cornflower bleached at the edges. I lean against the screen door and I let the sun soak into my skin as I watch a parade of earnest faces pass in and out of the house. Each one stops to tell me their own version of *the right thing to say.*

Hands touch my shoulders and arms wrap around my chest and fingers run across my back and lips touch my cheek and I am still not here. I want to be here and I need to be here but everything is just a bird's-eye view of dark suits and pastel dresses and browngrayredblonde heads.

A man my father's age:

"I've been there, buddy. Lost my dad a few months ago."

My dad was fifty-seven. Yours was probably in his nineties.

A middle-aged woman:

"Time heals all."

There it is! You were right, Dad.

A man who my father considered his closest friend:

"It's gonna be alright. Less cryin' and more tryin'."

I can't believe that's a thing someone would say or that this asshole just fucking said it.

A couple my age with two new babies:

"He's in a better place now."

Where? Sandals Resort? Fuck off.

A seventeen-year-old boy:

"I tried to commit suicide when I was fourteen and your dad saved my life."

Thank you. Thank you. Thank you. Thank you.

Another man my father's age:

"He was so proud of you. Never stopped talking about you. It's so nice to finally meet you."

Thank you. My dad never actually said those words to me.

A woman in her forties:

"It's a shame. He was so handsome."

Interesting thing to say. Thanks, you fucking weirdo.

A small parade of faces:

"At least he's not suffering anymore."

Not as much as I am standing here listening to you right now.

"It's just a part of life."

The last part, but yeah.

"He really *is* in a better place now."

Again with this one. A Disney cruise?

"At least it was quick."

It wasn't.

"Tomorrow will be better."

I remember my father's words and I smile. I share them with the woman who said it:

"It may not be *better* but it will be different. And different is really the only path to better."

She studies my eyes and puts her hands on my shoulders.

"*So* true. Your dad told me you were a wise one, Nate."

Fuck. Of course.

I weave my way through the crowd, into the house and lock myself in the upstairs bedroom. I sit down on the bed and watch the sun drape itself over Danny's skin as he sleeps cradled in Jen's arms. She smiles, motions for me to sit down beside her.

"You holding up okay, Glenn?"

"I just feel numb."

She pulls my head onto her shoulder and I slide my arm under hers and under Danny's tiny back.

"I remember the numbness. I still feel it sometimes."

I keep forgetting how much her mother's death has probably played a part in how she's been coping with all of this. I need to remember she has her own ghosts to silence every day too.

"I'm sorry, Jen."

"For what?"

"For everything. I didn't expect to disappear the way I have. I hate that I missed so much time with you guys."

"Doesn't matter. Can't change the past."

I feel the breeze drift through the window screen and run its fingers through my scalp.

I want to believe her.

I want to believe I'm safe.

I want to believe that someday I'll find a place where I can finally take a breath without worrying if there's going to be another one right behind it. Maybe this will be that place. All those people downstairs are here because they loved my father. His life affected theirs in ways I'll likely never know or understand. Their stupid clichés are flat because the surface of death is way too fucking enormous to paint. There aren't enough words. There will never be enough words. And there will never be the perfect arrangement of words to ever fit the shape of the void his absence has carved from each of us.

I walk back downstairs and I make my way through the crowd and I say *thank you, thank you so much.*

I say thank you to every single one of those faces.

Thank you.

Every single one.

I shake their hands and I hug them all.

Thank you, thank you, thank you.

Today is different.

my office, seven months later

I sit at my desk and I stare out the window overlooking the main printing floor. I find myself hypnotized several times a day from this humming terrarium of people and machines. Coworkers flitting around the lab, loading paper reams, filling inkwells, occasionally flipping me off or giving me the jerk-off motion when they catch me not actively staring at my computer.

Juan cracks open my office door and tells me he's got the best surprise for the next time we drop shit out of the window. I laugh, tell him he's fired.

Fuck.
A violent wave of nausea flies through me.
Fuck.
Out of nowhere.
What the fuck?

A wave flies through my body like the shadow of a freeway overpass. Fast cold black. I grab the trashcan next to the door. Fast cold black. I drop to my knees, vomit.
Fuck. What the hell was that?
Coffee and bile and a bitter metallic tang I haven't tasted since my first rounds of chemo.
I know that taste.
I'm on the floor and my head is between my legs and I am watching a drop of sweat form on the tip of my nose and fall into the carpet.

Another.

And another.

I lean over and I spit into the trashcan again.

I know this taste.

I close my eyes and I wait for the floor to stop rising and falling beneath me.

I stand up and fall back into my chair.

I know this feeling.

It's the same feeling I had the day I buried him. That feeling of not knowing what's next, not knowing how many sleeps are left before someone comes to rescue me.

Fuck. Where are you, Dad?

Another shadow of a freeway overpass. Fast cold black.

Are you ever coming back to get me?

I dry heave and I spit.

It's not safe here, Pop. Please come back.

Gag, spit, gag, spit, breathe, in through the nose, out through the mouth.

Are you ever coming back to get me?

I make it back to my feet and I tie the garbage bag shut and I carry it to the office men's room and stuff it deep into the trashcan under a pile of used paper towels. I see there's someone at the urinal so I walk into the stall, lock the door, sit down to pee, breathe.

In through the nose, out through the mouth.

I rub my chest to soothe my thrashing heart as if it's possible to soothe this kind of fear.

In through the nose, out through the mouth.

The white tile floor beneath my feet settles and hardens and I remind myself that my scans have been clear and my blood has been stable and my cancer is gone, even if its ghost remains. This is just the ghost and I'm the only one who can see it.

I am breathing and I am okay.

Ten minutes pass.

I turn around to flush the toilet.

No.

My breath disappears.

No. Nonononono.

My lungs flatten.

Black.

My urine is black.

Another shadow shoots through me. Fast cold black. I vomit again. Fast cold black. I choke and spit until I catch my breath. I sit on my hands to stop them from shaking and all it does is make my legs shake.

I sit and I sweat and I shake and I am alone and there is no map. I lie down on the bathroom floor and I stare up at the sprinkler fixture on the ceiling as tears pool inside my ears.

The only sound now is the rasp of my own breath.

I cry and I breathe until I stop shaking.

No one is coming to pick me up.

emergency room, one hour later

The nurse is finger-smoothing a strip of clear tape over the hole of my
IV and she's telling me not to worry, telling me she sees this all the time,
telling me dehydration is very common. I force a smile and I thank her
and I tell her I didn't realize dehydration could turn a person's urine
black. She points to the bag of saline hanging from the pole beside my
bed and she tells me I just have to get a couple of *those* in me before it
gets back to normal, before they can let me go.
I wait for her to leave and I wheel my IV pole over to the bathroom and
I sit down to pee. My urine is still black, still funereal.
My legs start to shake.
They're trying to run but there's nowhere for them to take me.
"Mr. Rockowitz?"
The ER doctor. Square jaw, prematurely gray hair, life-force barely
hanging on beneath his eyes. I introduce myself as he flips through some
papers and tells me I'm looking better already.
You've never seen me before.
He asks me how I managed to become so dehydrated and when I insist
that I'm not, he gives me a condescending smile.
"Okay, well nonetheless we'll get you hydrated and back on your feet in a
couple hours."
I know why he's reacting this way and I remind myself to play the part,
do what I'm supposed to do, pretend I'm okay.
"I'm sure you're right, Doc. I'm dehydrated. But I want to make sure it's
the only thing going on. Given my history and all."
He walks over to the computer, starts typing. The space between his

223

eyebrows puckers into a deep quotation mark. *He's confused.* He asks me which hospital I normally go to and I give him Jay's number, tell him *just call my doctor.* He pushes aside the curtain and walks off.

I see Jen through a small square window at the end of the hallway and I wave but she doesn't see me.

Twenty minutes pass and I'm on my back staring at the plastic backlit fresco on the ceiling above the CT scanner—*thank you, Jay*—a lush green garden under a cloudless sky. Some version of this Garden of Eden hovers above every scanner in every hospital I've ever been in. It's an illusion of beauty that never once resembles the tranquility it's supposed to invoke. It's a fake window into a fake sky that feels like a dream.

I want to trust that sky again some day.

"Are you okay, Glenn?"

I force a smile for the nurse who sees my tears.

She puts her hand on my arm and she tells me everything will be okay even though tubes are spilling out of me like a broken robot in a shuttered repair shop.

I lie still and I glide in and out of this giant white donut of a machine, holding and counting each breath as it leaves my body.

I'm not safe.

Breathe.

I want to feel safe.

Breathe.

I'll never feel safe.

The nurse lays me down on a gurney and wheels me back to my room under a slow-motion meteor shower of long fluorescent tubes bolted to the hallway ceiling.

I see Jen's face as soon as my bed turns the corner.

She looks at me with the same sense of knowing I felt in the bathroom when I stared at my reflection in my own black piss.

I'm not safe.

An hour later, as our cab passes under the red and white arm of the parking garage on the way out—the arm not yet a tongue and not yet alive—we assure each other *it'll all be okay* as we pretend not to hear the sound of the question mark hovering in the air between us.

Jen puts her hand on my thigh to silence the running.

"Don't let your mind go there, Glenn."

"You're right, you're right. I won't."

Too late.

My mind is already there, deep in the forest without a compass, without a flashlight, without fire, without a moon.

my office, the next day

The sun coming through the window outside my office door is yellow
and warm against my feet and my legs are firing away to the rhythm of
my machine-gun heart. There is nothing like the distorted shape of this
moment: I know how to peel off my skin when it's dying and I know how
to puke without making noise and I know how to sit still while I'm being
obliterated with radiation and I know how to make myself comfortable
on the floor of any public bathroom no matter how disgusting. I know
how to keep every kind of secret under the sun and I know how to
pretend my own fucking life. I know all of this. What I *don't* know how
to do is find a way to breathe in that space between a test and its results.
I don't know what to do in that tiny infinity between the gunshot and
the impact.

The intercom over my door crackles to life and a woman's voice directs
everyone to the main conference area for a company meeting. I stay at
my desk to watch the sun bend red at the horizon and turn the Hudson
River to blood.

My phone rings.

The ER doctor. Not the voice I want to hear.

I know exactly what it means when it's not a nurse who calls.

No no no.

I write the words he's saying on the back of an old flyer.

A 'mass'?

Right kidney?

It might be a new cancer.

What the fuck do you mean 'hopefully it didn't spread'?
It might be a new fucking cancer.

The floor beneath my feet rises and falls in sync with the rising tempo of my breathing, rising falling rising falling, people passing by my office talking laughing banging on my door, talking laughing rising falling rising falling. I'm writing more words and none of them make sense and my hand is shaking and I think I tell him thank you before I hang up, walk into my boss's office, close the door, flop onto his couch and look into his eyes.

He knows.

I don't have to say the words because he knows. He knows I've been waiting to hear the news and he knows he can't stop the night from swallowing what light is left in the sky outside.

I call Jen and I tell her the news and I listen to her cry as I pretend I'm not doing the same. I tell her I'm coming home. Something is using my body without permission again.

my office building, minutes later

I take the elevator to the lobby and I slam open the double glass doors
and I walk half a block, stop, bend over, put my hands on my knees,
catch my breath, keep walking. The air is cold and black and thick with
car exhaust and I don't know exactly where I'm heading but I know that
I have to make it home before the cement dries.
The world is a blurry time-lapse of headlights and taillights.
Red red white red white red red red.
Headlights and taillights in bursts of horizontal lightning.
This is not real. Electric red and white veins pulsing and dying.
Just a dream just a dream wake up wake the fuck up.
A shirtless old man with a cardboard sign speaks to my missing face:
"Help me out, brother."
I get to an intersection and the light is red. *Fuck.* I feel it coming, clawing
its way up from my stomach, battery acid, fear. *Fuck fuck fuck.* My body
is doing whatever it wants with me. *I never gave you permission.* I feel it
coming and I know I can't stop it. I lean over a trashcan, let it come
like napalm.
I never fucking gave you permission.
The couple standing a few feet away winces and walks away and I don't
blame them. *Please don't look at me. Please don't look at this fucking mess.*
I vomit until there is nothing left.
Headlights and taillights like electric veins all around me.
Nothing left inside my belly.
I follow the path of yellow circles along the sidewalk that lead me back

home. The breadcrumbs of streetlamps. I walk and I cough and I gag and I walk. I want to be home and I need to be home. I need to see Danny. I need to see the reason I bother to walk anymore. My son. The only love I have that is not fragile. Everyone else could leave me, would leave me, will leave me. I need to hold the only love I have that is not fragile.

Everyone leaves.

I need him.

Everyone leaves.

I need him and he is not here.

Everyone leaves.

I walk and I cry and I follow the breadcrumbs of streetlamps that lead me back home.

A rat darts out in front of me and I jump.

Snow from a fucking tree.

I stop, lean against a building, try to catch my breath, inhaling and exhaling. I tell myself the things my dad would say. *This is still the ghost, Glenn.* I inhale exhale inhale exhale. *You survived once and you'll survive again.* I inhale exhale inhale exhale. *This will pass.* I inhale exhale inhale exhale. *You are not going anywhere.* I inhale exhale inhale exhale inhale exhale inhale exhale. *Snow from a tree.* That's all it is.

I stand and I start running. I'm not going to let it dry. I am going to shake loose the wet cement and I am going to shake loose the memories of all those days alone in different hospitals, terrified and trying anything and everything to prove the numbers wrong, to stay alive one more fucking day, to do anything and everything to prevent my father from having to bury his son before his son could bury him.

I am going to shake loose all the other patients I met along the way, all the stories they told me, all the people they loved and abandoned against their will, all the false hope we gave each other sitting in those chemo chairs for hours on end shitting out platitudes, knowing full well that none of us knew a single fucking thing about the disease that was eating all of us alive.

I am going to shake loose the guilt I feel, that raging fucking house fire in my veins, wondering if my father's prayer is the reason I'm alive today. I'm going to shake loose the parts of me that died that summer of 1977, the deaths I watched, the deaths I overheard, the deaths I felt and smelled and witnessed with my own eyes, alone and frozen and fucking terrified. I'm going to shake loose the parts of me that died when I was dumb enough to believe I was protecting Jen by carrying this all myself.

I'm going to shake loose the parts of me that died when I chose to lie to Chris about my own health and not give him the chance to do for me what I was able to do for him: free him from the kind of secrets no one should have to carry alone. I'm going to shake loose the parts of me that die every time I behave in ways that resemble nothing of who I am in the truest corners of my soul. I am going to shake loose death in every form. I am going to shake loose death in every form and I am going to find love in everything, find love that isn't fragile.

I'm not going to let this cement dry.

my apartment building, twenty minutes later

I push through the revolving glass door, take the elevator up nineteen floors, walk down the hallway, unlock the front door, see Jen sitting on the couch reading a story to Danny in front of his small rotating Winnie the Pooh lamp. It's the only light in the room and it's flickering orange-red against their faces like the broken reflection of a sunset off the surface of a pool.

I take off my shoes and I tiptoe to the couch and I crawl up next to Danny and I try to kiss him and he pushes me away like a tiny Heisman trophy with curly hair.

I kiss him anyway, kiss Jen, walk to the bathroom, close the door.

I call Jay and I tell him the news and he tells me he already knows.

What the fuck?

I thank him sarcastically for calling me as soon as he heard.

"What was I *supposed* to do, G?"

"I don't know, JJ. Maybe call me and see if getting the news that I had a second unrelated cancer had an impact on my emotional state?"

"Did it?"

How can a man this smart be so dumb?

I turn off the ceiling light and I sit on the edge of the tub and I let my eyes adjust to the soft bourbon glow of the nightlight and I ask him to tell me what it all means.

"I don't know *exactly* what it means, G."

"Okay, cool. Have a good night, Jay."

"What?"

"What do you *mean* you don't know what it means?"

"I don't know what it means yet. We have to see how far it's spread or even if it's spread at all. It could be in your brain or in your bones or it could just be in your kidney."

"Wonderful, thanks. Okay, have a good night, Jay."

"I don't get this comedy bit you're doing, Glenn."

"It's not a 'comedy bit.' You're just not being helpful. It's like telling me that my headache could be hay fever or a brain tumor the size of a Buick."

"What do you *want* me to say, G? Just tell me and I'll repeat it."

"Lie to me! Tell me it's no big deal. Tell me it's an easy one to cure. Tell me it's so insignificant that you don't even normally treat it. I'm not fussy. Tell me anything other than I might be browsing hospice brochures soon."

He laughs.

Thank God.

This love suddenly doesn't feel fragile.

"Okay, G. The good news is that at least on the CT scan it *looks* like it hasn't broken the capsule."

"English, please."

"Sorry. Like it hasn't spread outside your kidney."

"But the kidney's gotta come out, right?"

"Yeah. If the PET confirms the tumor's active, we should take it out as soon as you can make it work with your schedule."

"My schedule? I'll do it as soon as he can get me on that table. My grandma used to say that if you don't have your health then you've got nothing."

"She was a smart woman."

"She was until she died of cancer."

I can hear him shaking his head.

"Your sense of humor is fucked up, G."

"If it weren't, I'd never stop crying."

"Okay, well I support whatever keeps you on this planet longer."

"I love you, JJ."

"Love you too, G."

Uh-oh.

He knows how I feel about this phrase and he's about to wish he would've hung up sooner.

"JJ?"

Long hesitant silence.

"… Yeah?"

"Did you just say 'love you too'?"

"Shit. Can we *please* not get into this again, Glenn?"

"Too late, JJ."

"Glenn, do you mind if I just set the phone down and come back after you're done with your speech?"

I hear the hint of a smile in his voice and I chuckle.

"Do whatever you want, JJ. I'm still gonna have to get into it. It's the law."

He sighs and I dive in.

"Are you *that* homophobic?"

"Oh, here we go—"

"Because it's okay to say those three words as three separate words, JJ. You can say *I love you* to another man and it doesn't *necessarily* mean you want to fuck him—"

"Okay, Glenn."

He's already defeated and I'm glad he is because it will make all of this go a lot quicker this time.

"—So you don't have to say things like *love ya* or *love you* or *love you too* or the worst, *me too.*"

"I really don't have time for this, G."

"I *guarantee* I have less time than you do."

He laughs.

"Fair enough. Wrap it up."

"So. When I tell you I love you, it just means that *I love you* and that I would take a fucking bullet for you and that I'll always have your back. You get what I'm saying?"

"Yup."

"Okay. Well, I love you JJ."

"I love you too, G."

"Good boy."

There's a big smile in the way he says goodbye.

I want all goodbyes to feel like this.

central park, afternoon

My mother's in town to help us out after the surgery and Ron and I have
been wandering the paths that snake throughout the park for hours, a
heroically long walk-and-talk distraction from my next couple of days.
I don't want to go back to another hospital tomorrow and I don't want to
be sliced open and I don't want them to inject another vial of watery gray
milk into my veins and I don't want to count backwards from a hundred
knowing I won't make it past ninety-seven before I fall back into that
place of wondering if the blinding halogen sun above the operating table
will be the last thing I ever see.
As we walk, the sun turns Ron's thin curls to gold filigree and deepens
the intensity of his deep black eyes. He's trying to soothe my rapidly
spiraling brain.
"This too shall pass, kiddo . . . I promise you."
Ron has been plagued with heart problems his whole life and has been
through so many surgeries, drug cocktails, infusions, transfusions,
implanted devices, cardiac flat-lines, code blues and shrugging doctors
with defeated *we-tried-everything* eyes, that I'm convinced he'll
outlive God.
"You're the herpes of people, Ronnie. If *anyone* knows—"
"Think of all the shit you've already been through, Glenn. Tomorrow will
be a tiny flash in your rearview."
A guy in rollerblades zips by in a midriff shirt that reads JESUS IS
COMING. LOOK BUSY.
I love this city.

"I'm sure you're right, Ronnie. It's just that going back into the hospital is bringing up a lot of weird shit for me. Dad stuff specifically."

"How so?"

"I just keep thinking that I let him die without giving him the chance to hear about that fucking summer and process it all. Or help *me* process it all. I just let him die without giving him the chance to know me the way he should've."

"Listen, dummy. You did the right thing by not telling him about all that camp stuff. Imagine if Danny unloaded all that onto you as you were dying."

"*I'd* be grateful."

"No you wouldn't. Not when it was something that happened so long ago and you were powerless to do anything about it."

We pass a guy in a knit poncho playing *Hotel California* on his guitar. *I hate this city.*

"I guess you're the lucky one who gets to go to the grave with that shitty secret, Ronnie."

"I'm so honored."

Talking about all this right now, so lightly and so abstractly, makes me feel embarrassed for carrying it around with me for so long or giving it as much weight as I have. The memory of those days ebb and flow in waves that are sometimes spaced weeks or months apart. And when they do hit, they're often just waves of guilt for not doing more to save Corey and Owen. Sometimes they're even just waves of guilt for not feeling anything at all. They're always painful but I just don't know if they're with me like a second skin the way they probably are for those two. Through it all, I've never seen myself as either a victim or a survivor. *Victim* makes me feel cut off at the knees, makes me feel impotent and helpless and unable to do the work I need to do to make the pain of those memories the smallest part of who I am. It also gives assholes like Randy and Chuck a power over me they don't deserve. *Survivor* doesn't feel right to me either because I don't know that I ever really survived that summer. Ever since that day behind the cabin, love feels unsafe and impermanent. Trust is always on the precipice of crumbling. Fear feels minuscule and oceanic at once. My sense of self feels both unbreakable and always on its heels. It all deserves its own eulogy but I'm not sure it deserves its own headstone. We walk together for another hour in silence as the city air gets cooler, heavier, wetter, and the sun falls into the skyline like an egg yolk sliding into a storm drain.

operating room, morning

I breathe in, breathe out, open my eyes. Everything is white. The blinding
halogen lamp. The cotton blanket draped over my body. The tiled walls.
The lab coats. Everything is white.
Everything, everything.
The blank slate before the surgeon opens me up and removes what we
hope is not the cancer it appears to be in the scans.
"How you feeling, Mr. Rockowitz?"
The anesthesiologist apparently. A chubby man in his late fifties with long
curly brown hair and tie-dyed scrubs.
"Not bad, Wavy Gravy."
He laughs.
"I bet a lotta people have had that thought, but no one's ever said it to
my face."
"Listen. If any doctor's gonna pump me full of drugs, I want him look
like he just got done bringing Santana to the stage."
He can tell I'm deflecting my fear with stupid jokes.
"Wait. You *are* a doctor, right?"
"I guess we'll find out together, Glenn."
I like this guy.
The surgeon enters the room, walks over to the side of my bed, says
hello and asks how I'm feeling. Dr. Gravy tells him I'm fine and tells him
I probably don't need any extra anesthesia.
They laugh, check monitors, confirm labels and wristband data.
One of their voices tells me something about counting backwards and

I count backwards until I'm swallowed by the clouds, until I'm swallowed by the whitewhite sun. I am not scared and everything is white.

Everything, everything.

recovery room, six hours later

I open my eyes and see that the sky outside the window is black again.
It feels so much further away now.
Everything feels so much further away now.
Everything, everything.
My thoughts are slow, splintered, numb.
I push my hospital gown aside with my thumb and stare at the broken
black train tracks scattered across my belly. I am sewn shut but I feel
wide open and I don't know if the cancer is gone but I know that I'm not.
Right now, that's all that matters.

hospital, next morning

I walk down the hallway and I watch my feet, *left right left right left right,* and I tell them what to do, *left right left right left right.* I am learning how to walk again. The parting gift of any long surgery.

I do one lap around the wing, two hundred feet that feel like two hundred miles. Minutes that feel like hours. *Left right left right left right.* As I walk, I have only one thought: *where is that little boy?*

I turn the last corner on my way back to my room and I see Jen standing there against the wall with Danny in her arms, making sure he's safe, making sure he's never alone. My chest swells when I see her eyes.

I squint, smile, wave.

Floating against the light blue wall, twenty feet away, *that little boy.* That little boy with enormous chestnut eyes, my eyes, the light blue wall like an ocean of time at his back.

Left right left right left right. Left right left right left.

His eyes widen with every left right left right.

He's scared.

His smooth little forehead crumples and the corners of his lips start to melt into his chin.

Why is he scared?

My stomach starts to burn.

He doesn't recognize me.

My son doesn't recognize the man that is getting bigger and taller with each new step.

I hold back my tears and I smile and he recognizes the shape of my mouth and smiles back.

His hands are shaking and his eyes are wide.

He's terrified.

That little boy with the enormous chestnut eyes. Shaking and scared, holding a small potted plant against his chest. Jen has her hand under his and is helping to keep it in place, helping to keep it from falling.

An aspidistra. My favorite plant.

He pushes it away from his chest, his tiny sausage arms fully extended and shaking, holding it like a peace offering to an unpredictable stranger.

"Danny boy."

My voice is soft and careful as our eyes meet.

I smile.

"It's me, Pup."

He hands Jen the plant and teeters over to me, *left right left right left right left right,* until he's in my arms, until he's tight against my chest, until his arms are around my neck, until he starts to cry, until my lips are against his head, until I start to cry.

Jen walks over, wraps her arms around us and speaks softly.

"You gonna show Daddy the plant you picked out?"

He smiles and his fear-shaking turns to excitement-shaking as he tries to form the word Jen just taught him.

"*Puhhdistra.*"

I love aspidistras and I've been without one since we moved into our tiny apartment. I pull the card from its trident:

> "Gordon had a sort of secret feud with the aspidistra. Many a time he had furtively attempted to kill it—starving it of water, grinding hot cigarette-ends against its stem, even mixing salt with its earth. But the beastly things are practically immortal."

A quote from George Orwell's *Keep The Aspidistra Flying.* A quote from the first author I ever loved. A quote I wrote down on a piece of notebook paper and tacked to my bedroom wall when I was eleven years old, clearly aware that I would not only have to survive this salted earth but find a way to thrive despite it.

Danny grabs my hand, unsteady on his newly-discovered legs, and leads me back to my bed *left right left right left right left* as we learn how to walk together.

my bed, ten hours later

I have been awake all night and I can barely keep my eyes open. I want to keep my eyes open and I need to keep my eyes open. I want to watch the early morning sky go from black to violet to blue to yellow to white. I want to watch this cloudless bruise heal. I want to watch the sun heal the sky.

I still don't know what the surgery will show and I still don't know if I'm at the beginning or at the end of this new race over the hot coals, but I want Danny to know his father. I want him to know his father even if it's a fraction of how much I knew my own.

I lean over and I slide the nightstand drawer open and I take out my yellow legal pad and half-chewed Bic pen and I start scribbling away to the rhythm of Jen and Danny's alternating snores:

"My beautiful boy,
I don't know where to start. I'm watching you sleep and I'm having so many thoughts. I don't feel like I have any kind of handle on what it is I want to say to you. I have so much to say and so much to share but I don't know how much time I have left and that's an awful feeling. Not knowing how much time you have. So what do I tell you in the time I *do* have left?

Great. I'm already not making sense. Well, maybe that's all you need to know about your dad. He made very little sense. I like that. Put it on my headstone. 'Here lies Glenn. He made very little sense.' No one would argue with you.

It's surreal to have you in my bedroom sleeping by my side the way I did with your grandpa when he was dying. I can't imagine what he was thinking. I can't imagine how he did it, especially worrying that I would be dead soon after or even before he died. If that had been us, I probably would've just thrown in the towel. I really don't know how he did it. I don't know how he stayed so lucid and so measured in the face of all of that. Your grandpa was a pretty amazing man. He was tortured by his unquiet mind but he was so fucking smart.

Oh, you'll probably remember that I curse a lot. I've been cursing since you were born and I'm still convinced you won't curse the way I do because I will have taken the fun out of it. It's not a taboo thing if you hear it all the time, right? One of grandpa's doctor friends used to tell me that people who curse do so because they're not smart enough to articulate their thoughts with real words.

That guy's a dick. Don't be that guy.

That's my first bit of advice. It's possible to know everything and still know nothing. So stay humble. Not false modesty humble, but genuinely humble. Humble yourself to the fact that you can always learn more and you can probably learn the most from people you least expect to learn from. I hope I'm alive long enough to tell you about Grandpa. I promised myself that I would write about him one day but it's looking more and more like my body's not going to give me the chance.

You may have already stopped reading so I don't know if anything I write beyond this point will matter. But fuck it. I love you more than I love anything or anyone on this planet and maybe all my shitty decisions will serve as a cautionary tale for you. Maybe they'll help you avoid at least some of the pain I've had to endure. I just hope you make a shitload of your own mistakes because I think the most important thing you can be in life is wrong. It may sound like cliché bullshit but it's true. Make glorious mistakes. Just make sure you don't ever intentionally hurt anyone along the way. Ever. That's the most important part. Don't ever intentionally hurt anyone. Ever.

By the time you read this it's possible Mom has already gotten remarried. And that's a good thing. She's an amazing woman and she deserves to be happy. I just hope he's not one of those dicks with the big calves and the ponytail and the hoop earring who never shuts up about wine. That guy's probably into cycling too. That's my worst nightmare for you. I know I should have bigger concerns but sadly right now that is all I can think of. He sounds horrible. I bet his name is Blake. Fuck that guy. See? Not making sense. This is your father. I bet you're proud.

Okay, what else? Don't trust any man who wants to work with kids. No normal adult man genuinely enjoys kids. And if they do, it's a big red flag. Stay away from that guy. Kids are mostly horrible and the only humans who have the strength and patience and emotional range to deal with them are women. It's why women are the better sex. Seriously. Close your eyes and think of any problem in the world and I guarantee you it traces back to a man.

I haven't tested these theories in a lab yet but I feel pretty confident I'm right.

What else should I tell you as your father? Drugs. Yes. Do them. But only in moderation. And if you're still doing them after you're twenty-five years old, kill yourself. Don't be that guy. And don't actually kill yourself. Ever. The people you leave behind will never be okay again. Never ever. No matter how horrific life gets—and it gets horrific—just hang on until tomorrow. And maybe the day after that or the day after that. Grandpa used to love to remind me that nothing in life is static. Everything happens in cycles. There will always be a Spring after a Winter, no matter how brutal that winter is.

I'm sure you're rolling your eyes and that's fine. If I'm boring you, go ask your new dad Blake to tell you about his backpacking trip through the Netherlands.

You back? Good.

Okay. What else? Music. Yes, music. Music music music. Immerse yourself in as much of it as possible, as often as possible. Make music if you can. And if you can't make music then make music out of whatever you do. If you want to spend your life detailing trucks, no problem. Just be the best you possibly can be at it. Make music out of it.

And since I'm on that subject, let's talk about shitty jobs. You'll have a bunch of them. And the quality of the job has very little to do with how much it pays. The best job I ever had paid me the least, and the worst one paid me the most. Just promise me that you won't be a victim. I hate victims. If your job is shitty, find a new one. Don't be that negative asshole at the office that takes everyone down with them. Someone is paying you. Do the best job you can. And if you don't like where your boat is headed, either take over steering the boat or shut the fuck up and row. Or ask Blake. I bet he'll sell you one of his kayaks. Sorry. I sound way angrier than I actually am. It's just the way your dad's brain works. Hopefully you get your mother's brain. It's not pretty in here.

What else? Surround yourself with people who are better than you.

Really. It'll make you work harder and it'll make you better. If you surround yourself with people who are worse, you'll get worse. Sure, you may feel better about yourself during the day, but at night you'll struggle with the fact that you're the tallest midget instead of the shortest giant. Be the shortest giant.

Also always say yes as often as possible. Grandpa Ron taught me this. I remember he was once offered a commercial job where he had to be on-camera driving a tractor and when his agent asked him if he knew how to drive one, he just said yes. Then he hung up and told me he had two days to learn how to drive a tractor. And he did. So say yes and figure it out later. Saying yes makes your world bigger the same way saying no makes it smaller. Of course I can think of a bunch of gross examples where this would be terrible advice but I trust that you get the gist of what I'm saying and that you'll use your judgment.

Like I said, none of this has been tested in a lab yet.

YET!

What else? Be generous. Like beyond generous. Like retarded-level generous. I know everyone thinks your father is generous to a degree that affects his life for the worse. And they're not wrong. But I believe the most important job you can do on this planet is to help other people get better. Safer, healthier, stronger, whatever. If everyone tried to do that even the tiniest bit, the world would be a pretty fucking amazing place. Ready for whiplash? Good. Here's the other thing: People are garbage. So don't ever be generous with the expectation that your generosity will be reciprocated. It usually won't. Expect nothing from people and you won't be disappointed. People who don't know me well think I'm a huge pessimist. Not even close. Your father is a disappointed optimist. And he's dumb enough to keep believing that people will do the right thing. They usually don't. But ... then you'll meet someone who does, and that's the person who will enhance your life in ways you can't possibly imagine. Aw shit. You woke up while I was writing that last sentence so I had to continue this and now I lost my flow. So if it gets worse, it's your fault. Actually, that brings up something really important: Own your shit. That means that if you screw up—and you will, and hopefully a lot—take responsibility for it. It's easy to blame someone else for your shit, but if you do, you'll be trying to jump from your knees. You'll become bitter and angry at a world that you could've changed if you had bothered to try. Your dad has a lot of friends who never stop complaining about how their lives have turned out so differently from how they expected.

Of course, *I* can't relate to that. When I was your age, I prayed every night that my life would be a never-ending battle with cancer and heartache. And you know what? It happened!

This is sarcasm.

I know. I'm a dick.

I'm no better than Blake. I get your point. You don't need to rub it in.

Oh! Random one but important: don't trust any adult male who's into Disney. Something's up.

Sorry.

You're probably glad I'm dead at this point, huh?

Let's talk about love. Grandpa Mel had a friend named Grant who would visit us every year with his wife and go on and on about how wonderful his marriage was and how the honeymoon phase never ended. He was so full of shit. Love is crazy and wonderful and hypnotic and magical and a million beautiful things all at once. But if it was meant to stay that way, we'd all be dead by the time we hit twenty-five. Remember what Grandpa Mel said? Nothing is static. Love is the perfect example of that. It will eventually calm to a real and natural place. And that's a good thing and a normal thing and a healthy thing. It only gets unhealthy if it gets completely static. If the bad parts of a relationship become the biggest parts then it's time to make a different choice. And if you find yourself in a relationship with someone who creates drama? Run. Or fake your own death. There's enough real drama in the world. You don't need to be with someone who manufactures it.

Also, never make a choice based on fear. Fear is the enemy of joy. And I promise you that all choices you make from fear will destroy you over time. Shitty job, shitty relationship? If fear has its way, you'll stay there. And you'll make choices that aren't the right choices for reasons of comfort. You have to push through no matter how much it hurts. In fact, I've found that the only way I know I'm doing the right thing is by how uncomfortable I am. So, do shit that makes you uncomfortable. Do a lot of it.

And don't worry about what other people have. I think there's a Buddhist saying about how comparison is the root of all pain. If you weren't sleeping so peacefully beside me, I'd go look it up. I guess you'll have to look it up for me. Or maybe Blake will have it tattooed on his inner thigh. I don't know. I can't do everything for you.

What else? Oh yeah. Don't get SO into sex that you have to buy equipment. It's great as it is. Put your energy somewhere else. Make the world more beautiful. Love the shit out of the people you love and then love the shit out of people you don't know if you ever could. There is so much darkness in this world. Be one of the ones who bring light into it. Okay, I'm running out of steam.

Well, if you only take one thing away from this weirdness, let it be the one truism that has never let me down: Don't take advice from someone you don't *in some way* aspire to be like.

Really. This has ALWAYS been true for me.

I'm so open to advice, but when I need advice on things that are really important to me, I'll only listen to people who I aspire to be like in some way. I hope that makes sense. I really think it's the only thing that's never *not* been true for me. Of course, that means that if you don't want to be anything like your father, then you should ignore everything I just wrote. And that's okay. I'm sure Blake can tell you cool stuff about pinot noir or martial arts or whatever.

I don't know. I'm looking at you right now and I'm watching your eyeballs go back and forth behind your lids and I'm wondering what you're dreaming about. I don't know how much more of this I'll get to see but I feel so fucking grateful that I even get to be with you right now. Even though I'm in pain and even though I'm really scared. I hope you get to experience a love this strong one day. And if you can't find it, please promise me you'll create it.

I love you,

Dad"

midtown dog park, early morning

I hold Danny against my chest and I wrap my jacket around him and
I feel the cold metal of the chain link fence against my belly as I lean
in to give us both a better view of the only dog in the park, a beautiful
brindled mastiff desperately trying to sniff out his lost ball.
"C'mon Otis! Leave it there."
A young guy about my age in his Wall Street best walks over, attaches
Otis's leash and leads him through the center of the piss-soaked field of
wood chips. We watch the two disappear into the morning fog as my
phone starts to buzz.
"G?"
"Jay?"
"They got it all."
Fuckfuckfuck.
"Like, the cancer is *gone* gone?"
"No more kidney. But, yeah, no more cancer."
Fuckfuckfuck.
I exhale in a way that feels like someone has peeled me open and blown a
million feathers right through the center of my chest.
They got it all.
I kiss Danny's head and I can taste the saltwater I'm leaving behind in
his curls.

natural history museum, one month later

The air in here smells like time, like all existence corralled and packed neatly into one place. Fossils and bones and creatures of all kinds are stuffed, reconstructed and posed in ways designed to make them feel fluid and dynamic and alive. I love how the largest and most dangerous creatures are now here in front of us, frozen and defanged, no longer a threat. I love this kind of alive and I hate this kind of alive and thanks to the tumors the surgeons cut out of my body last month along with the tumors that were sewn into my heart at camp that summer, I *am* this kind of alive.

Jen cranes her head over Danny's stroller and tries to break the staring contest he's having with the tyrannosaurus standing watch over the museum.

"That's enough with the dinosaurs, honey."

Danny furrows his brow as the late-afternoon sun pours in through the window and turns both their heads identical shades of gold. Jen tucks a strip of hair behind her ear and raises the pitch of her voice into Hard Sell mode.

"Don't you wanna see the zebras and tigers with Daddy? You guys always *love* that."

He looks up and sees me smile, sees me doing my part to close the deal.

"What's it gonna take to get you into these gently-used arms today?"

He sticks out his arms and lets out a fussy moan.

"Lazy little Hitler."

Jen chokes on her coffee, waves *stopstop,* swallows.

"You really have to stop with that."
I pull him from the stroller, kiss his sun-warm hair and lock him against my chest with both arms. A cage on a hospital clock.

Jen tells me she's going to find the restroom and will meet us at our *usual spot*. She knows exactly where we're headed.
Danny and I walk past the elephants and the wildebeest and the antelope. The animals that don't scare him.
He kicks away in my arms, air-running toward the ones that *do* scare him: the lions. The ones he seems convinced are my favorite.
He's running to the lions and I don't care.
I don't care because I know what to look for and I know what to smell for and I know what to listen for now. I can feel it perfectly, unmistakably and gene-deep the way I can now feel cancer cells in my own blood.
I know when something's not safe.
I know when something is trying to kill even the tiniest part of me.
We stare at the lions, the pack of taxidermized predators gathered under the shade of a small tree and I point out the bloodstains on their jagged teeth and the scars on their squat muscular bodies and the permanent winter in their browngold eyes.
I don't point out the small tree, the only one in the diorama, the one knotted and italic and completely unaware of the fact that it's the only thing separating the monsters from the sunlight.
I don't point out the small tree because I'm just grateful it's here.
Here as I am. Brittle fists up and ready.

EPILOGUE
a small writing desk in seattle, 2019

I get it. I don't like reading epilogues either. But I do like them more than prologues.

If you're here, it's likely because you just read a whole book, which is pretty rare these days. So, if you finished the book and want an update on what everyone's up to now, you're in luck.

If you're here because you're one of those nut jobs who *only* reads prologues and epilogues ("EpiPros" as they're known in the fetish community), well, then, you're going to be happy but very confused. Which we already knew, given your fetish and all.

For the rest of you, here's the update:

Randy was arrested in 1991—over a decade after I left camp— for various sexual crimes involving minors under the age of fourteen. He fled parole in 2017 and was on the run for almost two years before being recaptured at a Tennessee grocery store. He was actually caught the day after I sat down to write this epilogue in January of 2019. I believe the timing of his apprehension was divine intervention.

Why do you think that, Greg?

Well, I'm going to tell you. (And it's Glenn)

You see, when I heard he was on the run, I started making plans to fly out to confront him, assuming either of the two leads I had regarding his whereabouts had panned out. I wanted to confront him *not* for some bullshit machismo revenge. Not at all. I wanted to confront him because I desperately wanted to look him in the eye, talk to him and really try to understand him.

I know. I'm an idiot.

My shrink didn't like this idea either.

"What the *fuck* do you think you're going to get out of that piece of human garbage? A deep reflection of past behavior and a profound, heartfelt apology? A long explanation of his own childhood that would allow you to feel enough empathy to unburden your shitty soul with some fucked up, half-ass form of forgiveness?"

Okay, it's *possible* those weren't his exact words. He may have said all of that more eloquently, sans the colorful language. Either way, he was right. Randy is a colossal piece of shit who deserves to spend eternity in the fiery bowels of Hell or trapped walking down an infinite office hallway carrying a sheet cake and having to courtesy-laugh every time some dick in khakis says, "Is that for *ME?*"

Okay, that's just my idea of Hell. But whatever.

The bottom line is this:

Randy will never know a cageless sky for the rest of his natural life and I'm okay with that.

Although Corey struggled quite a bit during his adolescence and late teen years, he eventually found a great support system and, as my father would say, turned his pain into tailwind. He is now an attorney (we all make mistakes), living on the East Coast with his wife and three children.

Owen has had a longer journey re-finding the light he lost that summer. He has been divorced three times and is currently unemployed. He does, however, have two wonderful sons from his first marriage and has found great comfort in our reconnection, or what he calls the *worst class reunion ever.* He's a sweet soul, and I'm lucky to know him.

Jen and Danny are alive and thriving and one of them is now 6'2" and has a full mustache and beard. They asked I not say which. I was never supposed to be alive to see any of this and I feel gratitude—*genuine* gratitude—every single day. Even on my shittiest days, I feel very lucky to see that boy's sweet face and to still be on the oxygen side of the earth.

Jay and I speak several times a week and he has been instrumental in helping me survive three additional cancers. He has two wonderful daughters, either of whom I hope to one day force into an arranged marriage with Danny.

Nate now lives on the East Coast with his wife and three wonderful children. As an orthodox Jew, he continues to struggle with the fact that we even celebrated Easter in the first place.

Julia is happy and healthy and living in the Southwest with her husband and three children. As per our father's wishes, she received a hand-written birthday card from him every year until she turned eighteen.

Andrea never re-married after my father's death because, as she says, "no man will ever come as close to human perfection as your father." Okay, she never said that. Or even implied it. Or ever felt anything close to it. But still.

Mom is doing mostly well living in a Ronnie-less house outside of Phoenix. Even though his death is what led to the events that allowed me to write this book in its current form—the form it was always meant to be—I would trade all of it to have him back for even one more day. Anything longer than a day and I'd probably wind up killing him.

The aspidistra bloomed a tall white flower as I was finishing this book. It's the very first flower the plant has ever produced since I took it home from the hospital so many years ago. Aspidistras do not produce tall white flowers.

Dad continues to make his presence known in strange and beautiful ways, apparently.

CPSIA information can be obtained
at www.ICGtesting.com
Printed in the USA
BVHW031421071221
623423BV00014B/489/J

9 780578 257082